C0-ASB-995

OUT ON A LIMB

Help the squirrel get to the acorn.

End

Take your kid's education to the next level with Anywhere Teacher!

Anywhere Teacher's complete learning system provides grade-specific skill practice in math, reading, writing and more. Created by School Zone in collaboration with teachers, it has been developed to align to national curriculum standards. Guided adventure paths offer step-by-step progression through each grade level. Kids can explore thousands of activities for a fun, safe, and ad-free learning experience. Anywhere Teacher, combined with School Zone's printed learning materials, delivers **Two Great Ways to Learn!**

Get 30 Days Free on Anywhere Teacher®

1 Hover a tablet or smartphone camera over this QR code, then select the link or go to **anywhereteacher.com**.

2 Click the **Subscribe** button.

3 Fill out your information.

4 Enter the coupon code **SZ12501AT** to get a 30-day free membership and full access to our entire learning library.

CANDY SHOP

Get to the center of the lollipop.

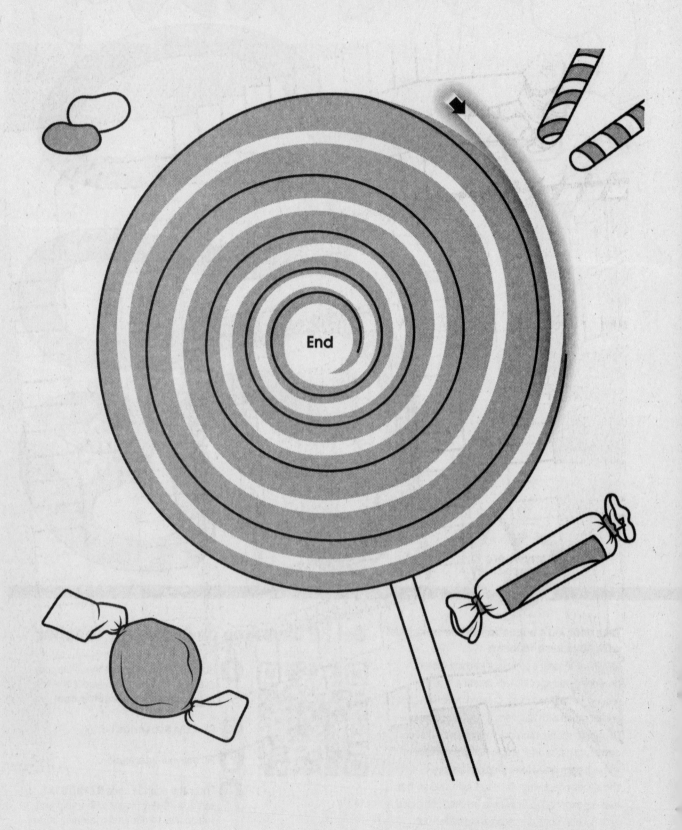

©School Zone Publishing Company 12501

LONG WAY DOWN

Help the boy get to the first floor.

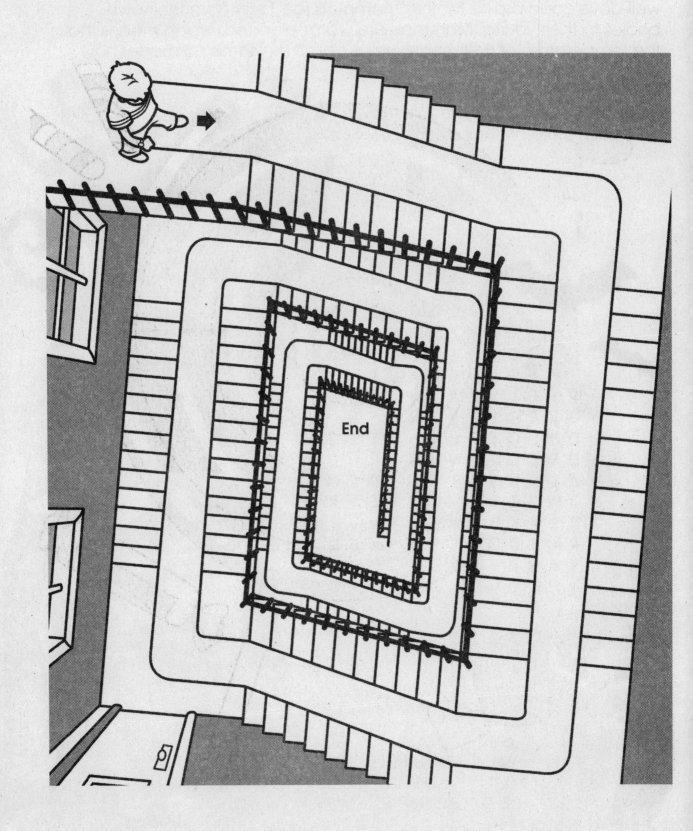

©School Zone Publishing Company 12501

FURRY CRITTERS

All mammals are alike in five important ways. Mammals have hair on their bodies for at least a part of their lives. They also have large, well-developed brains. Mother mammals feed milk from their own bodies to their young. Mammals are warm-blooded, which means that the temperature of their bodies stays about the same no matter how warm or cool the weather. Mammals care for their young. They protect them and teach them the skills they will need to live on their own.

```
          D K A S
        C G J B G L N U
      X M F W S X I C T Y S
    D L B K I J O F R S D C D
    W E G Y N S F H L A M V A
    P F C L V B A T V D F S T T
  M G K S Q E U B X P L F B U J
  U D M D O L P H I N R E W C
  S Y D R O C X I H M S X R H D
  J W A L R U S J T A K T M J O
  P J W R G S K M O N K E Y X R A K I
  X F L A K C E B N H T R L I H S P Y L
  R M S D O G L I V S K U N K M E E O
  Y A N S V F J D M G O A T H S C N
    H C L N          O D J
    P C U            R E P
    Y Q O Y          U E B
    R T O            H R
    A S G N          Y P W
```

APE	DOG	GOAT	RACCOON
BAT	DOLPHIN	HORSE	SKUNK
CAT	ELEPHANT	MONKEY	WALRUS
DEER	GIRAFFE	MOUSE	WOLF

4

©School Zone Publishing Company 12501

Answer each clue with a mammal from the
word search. Then write the letters in the boxes.

A. I can swing in trees using my tail. _____

B. My face is marked like a bandit. _____

C. I make clicking sounds underwater. _____

D. I am the largest land animal. _____

E. I am the tallest land animal. _____

F. You might mistake me for a flying mouse. _____

G. I like to float on ice. _____

H. I am the only animal with bones called antlers. _____

©School Zone Publishing Company 12501

WHAT A RIDE!

Go up and down with the roller coaster.

End

©School Zone Publishing Company 12501

FOR THE BIRDS

Help the bird find the nest.

End

©School Zone Publishing Company 12501

HIKING THROUGH THE FOREST

Find and circle the hidden pictures.

peach   cookie   glue   clover   pliers   lamp   kettle   unicycle

8

©School Zone Publishing Company 12501

NOISE IN THE BASEMENT

Help the person get to the basement light.

End

©School Zone Publishing Company 12501

CLAM UP

Help get to the clam.

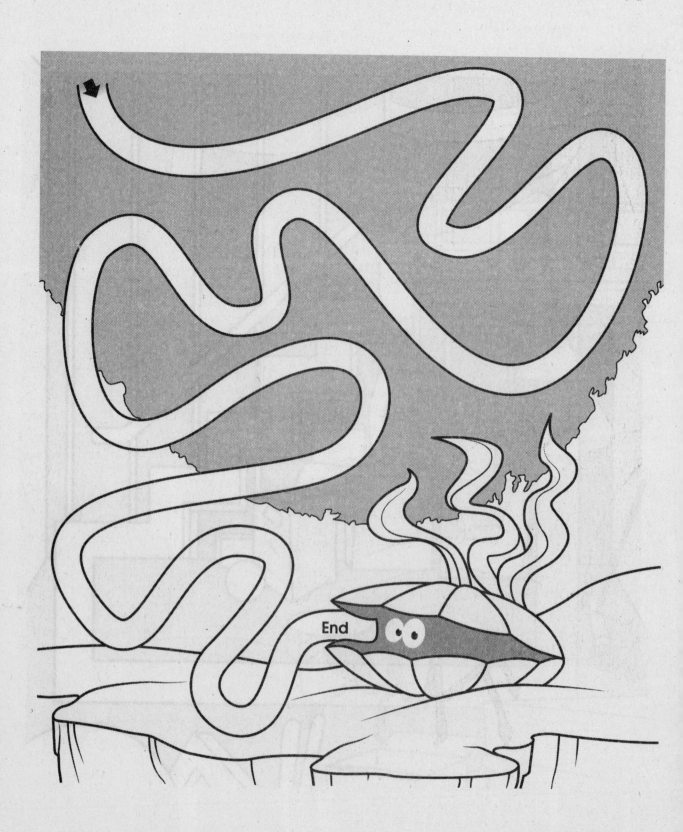

End

©School Zone Publishing Company 12501

WEB WORK

Get to the center of the web.

End

©School Zone Publishing Company 12501

EXPLORING THE CAVE

Follow the explorer through the cave.

End

©School Zone Publishing Company 12501

Connect the dots from **I** to **10**.
Color the picture.

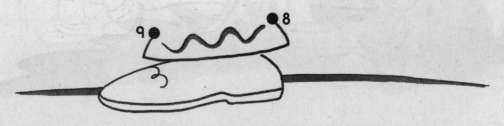

©School Zone Publishing Company 12501

Connect the dots from **1** to **10**.
Color the picture.

14

©School Zone Publishing Company 12501

FIRST PLACE

Help the car finish the race.

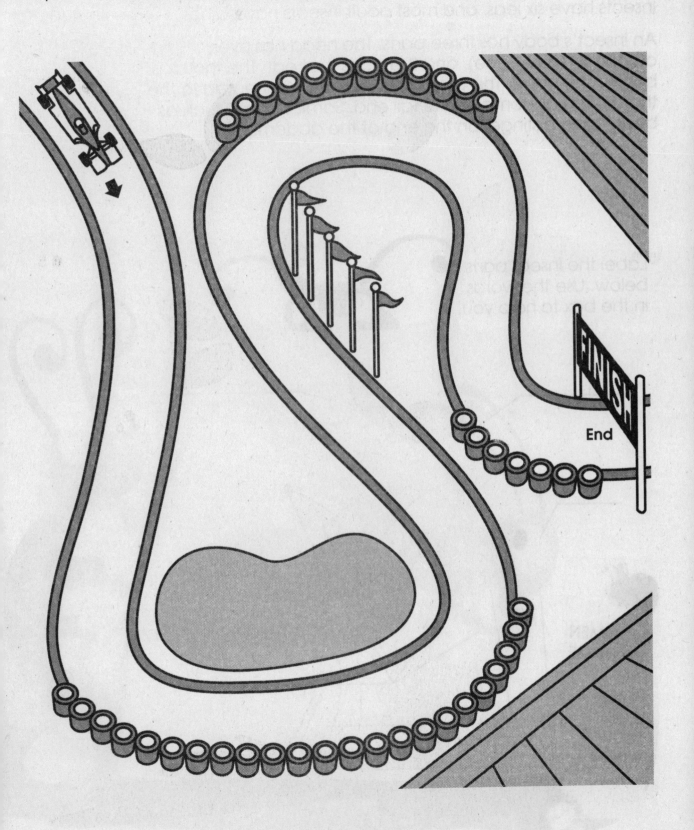

End

©School Zone Publishing Company 12501

GOING BUGGY

Both people and insects are animals, but they differ in many ways. Insects have a hard outside shell instead of bones. Insects have six legs, and most adult insects have wings.

An insect's body has three parts. The head has eyes, antennae (an-ten-ee), and the parts that eat. The thorax is behind the head. The wings and legs are connected to the thorax. The abdomen is the tail end. Some insects, such as bees, have a stinger on the end of the abdomen.

Label the insect parts below. Use the words in the box to help you.

ABDOMEN
ANTENNAE
EYE
HEAD
LEGS
THORAX
WINGS

SEE GLOSSARY

16

©School Zone Publishing Company 12501

One of the largest insects is the Goliath beetle. It can grow over four inches long.

One of the smallest insects is the fairyfly. It can hardly be seen with the naked eye.

SEE GLOSSARY · SEE GLOSSARY

ANT
BEE
BEETLE
BUTTERFLY
CICADA
COCKROACH
CRICKET
DRAGONFLY
FIREFLY
FLY
GRASSHOPPER
KATYDID
LADYBUG
MAYFLY
MOSQUITO
MOTH
TERMITE
WASP

```
              B C A M
          B F T M V I F I Y B
        B C U Y L G O U C Q C J H Y
      F D R C J G Y D S W A S P D B N
    L O N I V L R T E B Q T D I F U F T
    P E Y M C B H A E H V S U Y A S T J B
  G A N T K X K S D T E R F I F Y T T N M
  S B J H F E V F S T Y F G H Y T H E J K B
  T L C K M T Y N H X R B I L G K O R V D E
  V H D C O C K R O A C H U F D U J F N Y E
  N I S R T T G K P W F V H G J G K L F A K T
  W G H N H I F W P L Y C K M L A T Y P R H E
  P M B D I B U I E T J S M M A M D M I B U
    F C E B L S D R A G O N F L Y N Y W K C
    I Y T E R M I T E D E F E O U F G T I
    P B J T X T H P F V S T H T P L H Y
      M N S L H O D I L B I F B H J Y
        O Y D E L K A T Y D I D R
          S T F H R I F S K
```

There are at least four times as many kinds of insects today as all other kinds of animals combined!

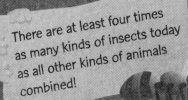

A cricket's "ears" are located on its front legs.

17

©School Zone Publishing Company 12501

HIDE AND SEEK

Find and circle the hidden pictures.

 medal   trident   scorpion   antlers   mask   walnut   cowboy hat   dove

©School Zone Publishing Company 12501

GOING FISHING

Help the fisherman get to the end of the dock.

End

©School Zone Publishing Company 12501

Connect the dots from 1 to 10.
Color the picture.

©School Zone Publishing Company 12501

THE WAY HOME

Help the ant get through the tunnel.

End

©School Zone Publishing Company 12501

Connect the dots from **1** to **10**.
Color the picture.

22

©School Zone Publishing Company 12501

MONKEYING AROUND

Find and circle the hidden pictures.

arrow

apple

lipstick

cloud

fork

hat

safety
pin

dumb-
bell

©School Zone Publishing Company 12501

AHOY, MATES!

Find and circle the hidden pictures.

 envelope

 seven

 tongs

 spider

 lipstick

 baseball bat

 laddle

wrench

24

©School Zone Publishing Company 12501

Find and circle the hidden pictures.

pepper   shoe   watermelon   guitar   hot dog   apple   olive   camera

25

©School Zone Publishing Company 12501

Slime and Scales

Reptiles and amphibians are cold-blooded, which means that their body temperature varies with their surroundings. Like many animals, reptiles and amphibians have backbones.

Amphibians include frogs, toads, salamanders, and caecilians. Most amphibians spend the beginning of their lives in water and then live on land as adults. They have smooth, moist skin without scales.

Reptiles have overlapping scales that make their skin dry and rough. Some reptiles are snakes, lizards, turtles, crocodiles, and tuataras.

Think About It!

What kinds of reptiles and amphibians live near you? Why do you think they live in your area?

ALLIGATOR   SALAMANDER
BULLFROG   SKINK
CROCODILE   SNAKE
FROG   TOAD
GECKO   TORTOISE
IGUANA   TUATARA
LIZARD   TURTLE
NEWT

SEE GLOSSARY · SEE GLOSSARY

Reptiles and amphibians live on every continent except Antarctica. In hot climates, they stay in the shade or are active at night. To survive cold winters, many species hibernate.

```
            A T B C W K
        I G U A N A V G X U B H I C V
      V E V S F H S W C O E U L C S W R T C
    D I L T A I K D K D N A S C H L D N O S A H
    E M D E K L E S N I E F G I R K I F T A H E S
    F A L S A L A M A N D E R F J B O E R Y K J H
    G Q K I G I W H G K H G M O G T R S T O G E K
    H R T H Z G D E Y H G E K T G Y O T K E G X
    A U R J A N G R K W M V K B X I A B T Y
    N S A J C T R J C R O C O D I L E J D U S J I
    K W K T F G O K D Y P L D S T U H O K W R K H B
    B L F A M L R Y A Q F L H E O N L M L E T L F J T
    M T O R T O I S E J K Y N L W M E S F M L A M M R
    S U Y A B U J K         N M O T W N G E N F D
    O O Q O W A                 I R H T H K I O H
```

26

©School Zone Publishing Company 12501

Use the code to learn the names of some unusual reptiles and amphibians.

A	D	E	F	G	I	K	L	N	O	R	S	T	U	Z

1. This amphibian grips smooth surfaces with sticky suction pads on its toes.

☐ ☐ ☐ ☐ ☐   ☐ ☐ ☐ ☐   ☐ ☐ ☐ ☐

2. If threatened, this reptile spreads a flap of skin around its neck.

☐ ☐ ☐ ☐ ☐ ☐ ☐   ☐ ☐ ☐ ☐ ☐ ☐

3. This reptile has spines on its back and can live for over 100 years.

☐ ☐ ☐ ☐ ☐ ☐ ☐

4. This amphibian lives in mountain streams with fast currents.

 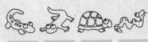

☐ ☐ ☐ ☐ ☐ ☐   ☐ ☐ ☐ ☐

5. This type of young newt can grow a new leg if one is injured.

☐ ☐ ☐

6. This poisonous reptile gives a warning before it strikes.

☐ ☐ ☐ ☐ ☐ ☐ ☐ ☐ ☐ ☐ ☐

©School Zone Publishing Company 12501

RETURNING TO EARTH

Help the rocket find its way through space.

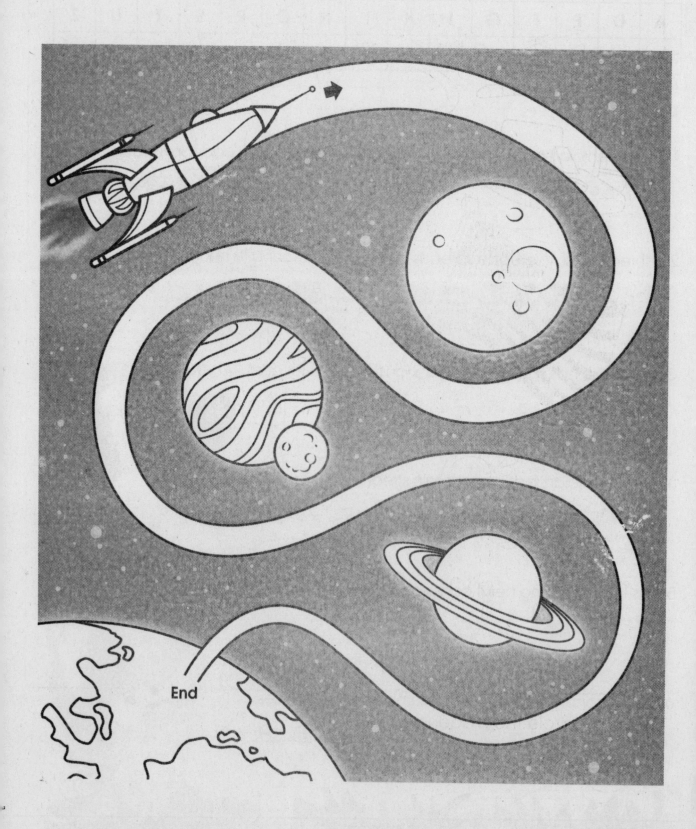

End

©School Zone Publishing Company 12501

SPACE DISCOVERIES

Find and circle the hidden pictures.

hard hat   brick   candy corn   pincushion   wave   sweet potato   buffalo   ornament

©School Zone Publishing Company 12501

Connect the dots from **1** to **10**.
Color the picture.

30

©School Zone Publishing Company 12501

HALL OF MIRRORS

Find and circle the hidden pictures.

 harp

 joystick

 in-line skate

 CD

 unicycle

 can

 bottle

engine

31

©School Zone Publishing Company 12501

Connect the dots from **1** to **10**.
Color the picture.

©School Zone Publishing Company 12501

UNDERWATER ADVENTURE

Find and circle the hidden pictures.

fence   pear   scooter   pretzel   campfire   snake   palm tree   necktie

©School Zone Publishing Company 12501

THE BEANSTALK

Help Jack climb down the beanstalk.

End

©School Zone Publishing Company 12501

Connect the dots from **I** to **10**.
Color the picture.

©School Zone Publishing Company 12501

HOPPING AROUND

Help the frog hop across the lily pads.

End

©School Zone Publishing Company 12501

AN AFTERNOON IN THE WORKSHOP

Find and circle the hidden pictures.

 bell   jack-o'-lantern   box   vacuum   house   glasses   microphone   penny

©School Zone Publishing Company 12501

BIRDS OF A FEATHER

Birds are special animals because they have feathers. Most birds use the feathers on their wings for flying. Feathers also keep birds warm in cold weather and dry in water.

Birds use their beaks to eat different kinds of food. Birds that eat hard seeds have short, cone-shaped beaks. Hawks and owls have hooked beaks for tearing apart their prey. Ducks have flat beaks to filter tiny plants and animals from the water.

Birds' feet come in many shapes and sizes. Birds that perch on tree branches usually have three toes in front and one toe behind for a good grip. Long, wide toes keep a heron from sinking in mud. Birds of prey have long, curved claws called talons. Ducks and water birds often have webbed feet.

Think About It!

Why do birds fly? Does flight give them an advantage over other animals?

```
H A
V E
B K R M P
L I M O E R
U N W J N
E G S H G
L J F T Q U J M
H A I S U I H O
W P Y S C V N I
N U T H A T C H B
V W O S E A G U L L
P H O L D R J W K P
C D G O M D T B X K M
D R O A D R U N N E R
W O O B F P F C O I B
K C P N B H P E I K L K
S J F A M I Y V C K G
J R T A N R N P I K C R E K D I
Q S G      D J O S T R I C H D W T E H D U O S
W U D L S D Q C Y S P A R R O W N A T I C R F V B L N T
  A H U M M I N G B I R D I S M Z N L N Y R B U H U O
  C V I H S N D T P G O L D F I N C H A J A Q O W L I
W P E L I C A N      C K      F J M E L I J
```

BLUE JAY	HUMMINGBIRD	OWL	ROADRUNNER
CARDINAL	JACANA	PELICAN	ROBIN
DUCK	KINGFISHER	PENGUIN	SEAGULL
GOLDFINCH	NUTHATCH	PIGEON	SPARROW
HAWK	OSTRICH	QUAIL	WOODPECKER
HERON			

SEE GLOSSARY. SEE GLOSSARY

©School Zone Publishing Company 12501

The bar-headed goose is believed to be the highest flyer. It has been known to fly at an altitude of over 25,000 feet.

The peregrine falcon is thought to be the fastest diver at over 200 miles per hour.

The bee hummingbird is the smallest bird with a length of about 2 inches and a mass of about 2 grams.

The male African ostrich is the largest bird. It can be 9 feet tall and weigh 300 pounds.

The emperor penguin can dive underwater at depths of over 1700 feet.

Help the bird find the way back to its nest.

©School Zone Publishing Company 12501

Connect the dots from **1** to **10**.
Color the picture.

©School Zone Publishing Company 12501

BUZZING AROUND

Help the bee get from flower to flower.

End

©School Zone Publishing Company 12501

THE OCEAN DEEP

Follow the submarine through the water.

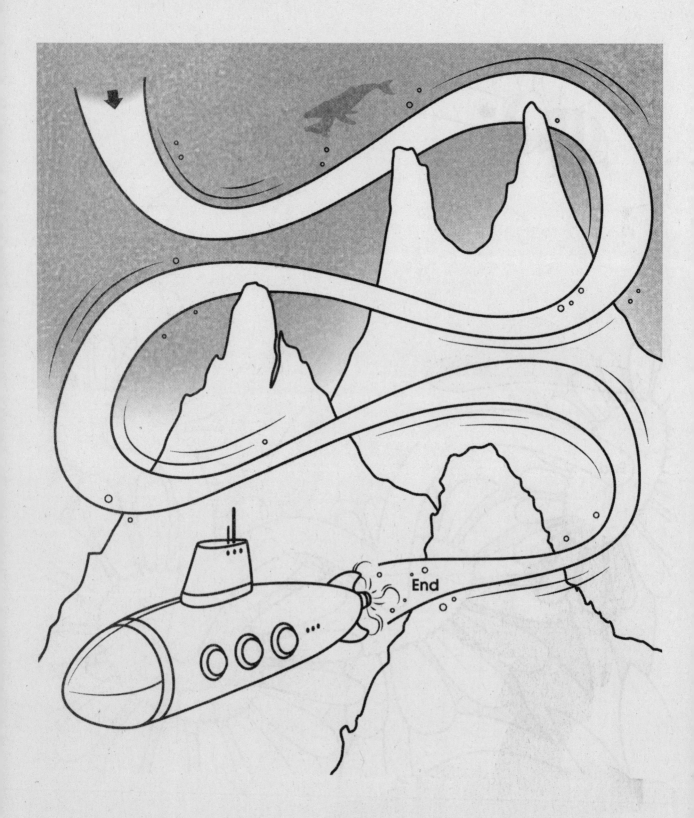

©School Zone Publishing Company 12501

Connect the dots from **1** to **10**.
Color the picture.

Connect the dots from **1** to **10**.
Color the picture.

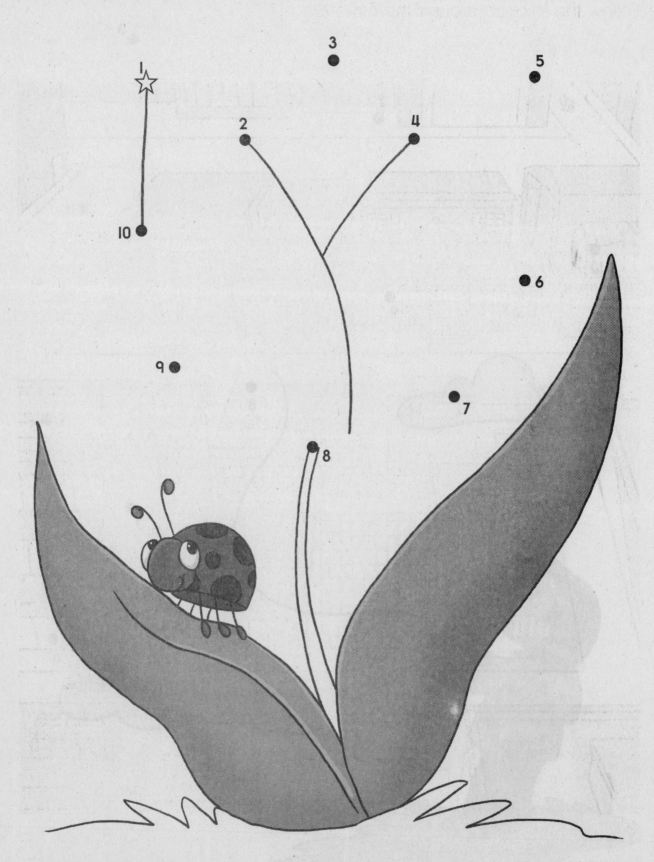

©School Zone Publishing Company 12501

TOURING THE CITY

Follow the taxicab around the city.

©School Zone Publishing Company 12501

AIR SHOW

Follow the airplane as it makes shapes.

End

©School Zone Publishing Company 12501

THE BIG CHEESE

Find and circle the hidden pictures.

doughnut   candy   wheelbarrow   slipper   megaphone   barn   lotion   wallet

VISITING THE RUINS

Find and circle the hidden pictures.

lemon   lotion   lightning bolt   dumbbell   pillow   watermelon   nail   orange

48

©School Zone Publishing Company 12501

Find and circle the hidden pictures.

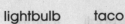

lightbulb

taco

candy
corn

magnifying
glass

rocket

snake

milk
carton

acorn

©School Zone Publishing Company 12501

49

OUT ON A LIMB

Find and circle the hidden pictures.

hammer   lightning bolt   purse   sock   pencil   cap   baseball   journal

©School Zone Publishing Company 12501

Connect the dots from **1** to **15**.
Color the picture.

©School Zone Publishing Company 12501

CONSTRUCTION ZONE

Find and circle the hidden pictures.

bed

brick

comb

tire

stool

yo-yo

wagon
wheel

map

52

©School Zone Publishing Company 12501

Find and circle the hidden pictures.

 journal
 bolt
 flute
 arrow
 vest
 hammer
 screwdriver
jar

©School Zone Publishing Company 12501

WATERY WORLD

Close to shore or far from land, at the sunny surface or miles down in inky blackness, the ocean is filled with plants and animals. Most ocean animals are fish—about 15,000 different kinds have been identified so far. Fish usually live in the shallow water over the continental shelf.

Many animals besides fish live in the ocean, including tiny plankton and huge whales. Sharks are fish, but they don't have bones. Instead, a shark's skeleton is made of cartilage. Whales and dolphins are mammals. They are warm-blooded, they breathe air, and they give birth to live young. Many ocean animals are invertebrates. They don't have backbones. Some invertebrates are jellyfish, starfish, and squid.

Think About It!

How do oil spills and other forms of pollution affect ocean plants and animals?

BARNACLE
COD
CORAL
CRAB
DOLPHIN
EEL
KELP
LIMPET
OCTOPUS
PLANKTON

SAILFISH
SEA ANEMONE
SEA FAN
SEAHORSE
SEAWEED
SHARK
SHRIMP
SQUID
STARFISH
WHALE

SEE GLOSSARY

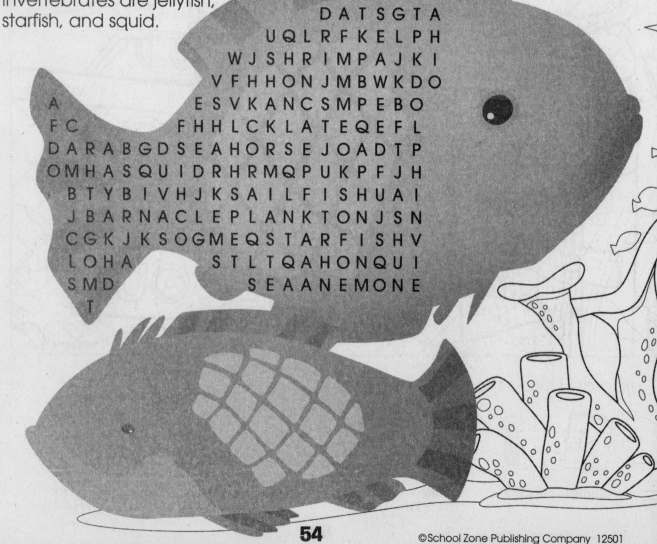

```
          D A T S G T A
        U Q L R F K E L P H
        W J S H R I M P A J K I
        V F H H O N J M B W K D O
      E S V K A N C S M P E B O
  A   F H H L C K L A T E Q E F L
  F C
  D A R A B G D S E A H O R S E J O A D T P
  O M H A S Q U I D R H R M Q P U K P F J H
  B T Y B I V H J K S A I L F I S H U A I
  J B A R N A C L E P L A N K T O N J S N
  C G K J K S O G M E Q S T A R F I S H V
  L O H A     S T L T Q A H O N Q U I
  S M D       S E A A N E M O N E
  T
```

©School Zone Publishing Company 12501

Circle the hidden ocean creatures.

jellyfish

manta ray

clownfish

crab

starfish

reef shark

sea
anemone

angelfish

green
turtle

©School Zone Publishing Company 12501

UNDER THE SEA

Help Simon Seahorse swim to his friends.

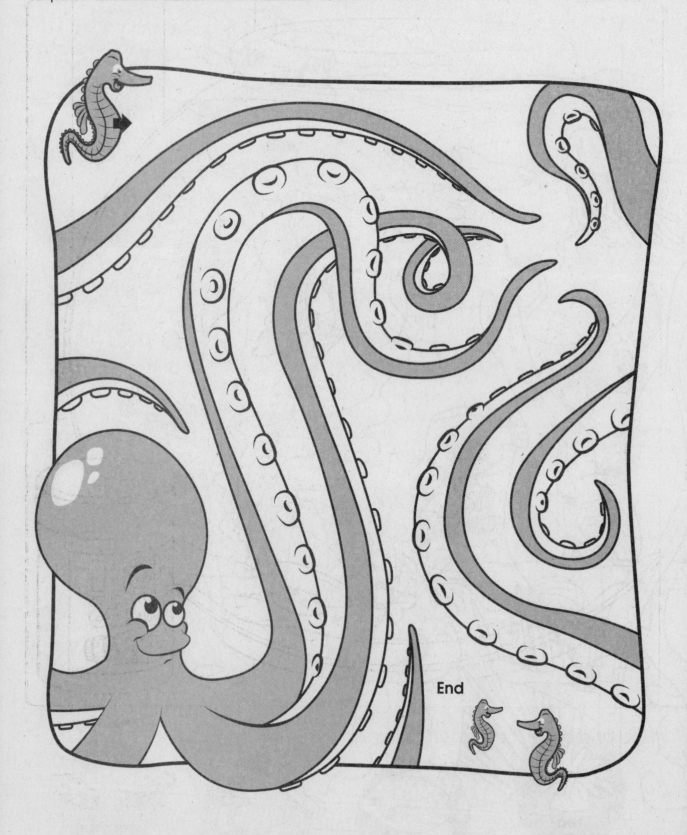

End

©School Zone Publishing Company 12501

A BOWL OF FUN

Find and circle the hidden pictures.

  teddy bear

 peanut

 barrel

 dress

 necklace

 pipe

 bat

 cookie

©School Zone Publishing Company 12501

UNDERSEA FUN

Find and circle the hidden pictures.

hamburger   fire   paintbrush   ribbon   fire extinguisher   football   snail   submarine

©School Zone Publishing Company 12501

Connect the dots from **1** to **15**.
Color the picture.

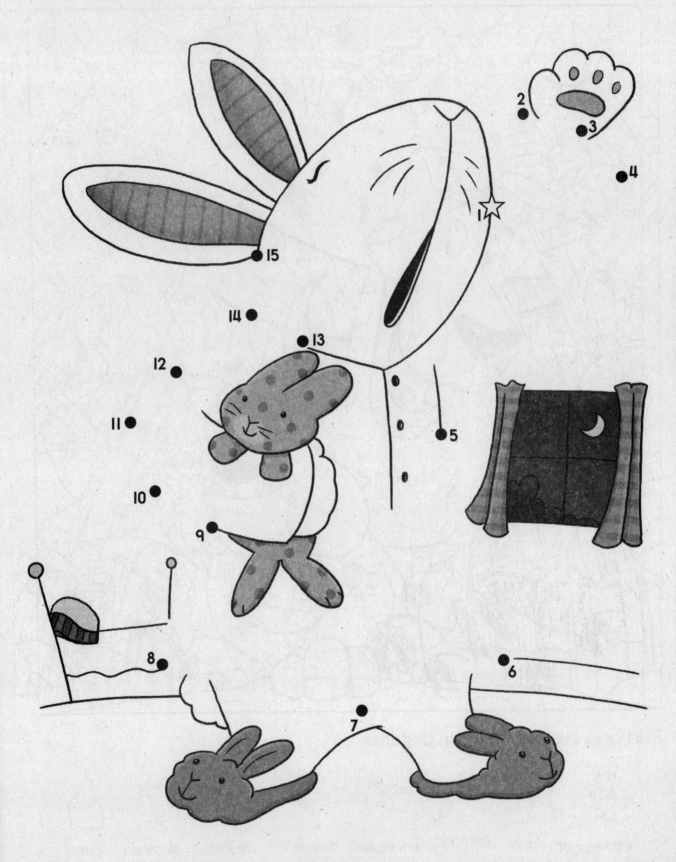

©School Zone Publishing Company 12501

PUPPY PARADE

Find and circle the hidden pictures.

sock   drumstick   paddle ball   envelope   helmet   yo-yo   arrow   pear

60

©School Zone Publishing Company 12501

VENICE VOYAGE

Help pilot the gondola to the dock.

End

©School Zone Publishing Company 12501

Connect the dots from 1 to 15.
Color the picture.

©School Zone Publishing Company 12501

FAIRY DUST

Find and circle the hidden pictures.

home plate

glue

watermelon

pizza slice

music player

footprint

lightbulb

puffin

63

©School Zone Publishing Company 12501

SURF'S UP!

Find and circle the hidden pictures.

necklace　　seashell　　snorkel　　flipper　　dolphin　　island　　starfish　　sailboat

©School Zone Publishing Company 12501

THE OTHER SIDE

Help the chicken cross the road.

End

©School Zone Publishing Company 12501.

RAINFOREST ANIMALS

Rainforests are regions of forest with year-round warmth and large amounts of rainfall. More kinds of birds, insects, mammals, reptiles, and plant species live in the world's rainforests than in any other region. Many rainforest animals are unknown or endangered. Scientists worry that these unique creatures may become extinct because of the destruction of the world's rainforests.

Rainforests can be divided into four layers. The canopy is the top layer. A few very tall trees rise above the canopy. They are called emergent trees. The understory is the middle layer between the canopy and the rainforest floor that is shaded by larger trees. The floor is very dark because the trees above block most of the sunlight. Each rainforest layer supports different plants and animals.

SEE GLOSSARY · SEE GLOSSARY

Think About It!

Why do you think people cut down rainforest trees?

How are rainforest creatures different from other animals?

Label the layers of the rainforest.
- A. understory
- B. canopy
- C. floor
- D. emergent trees

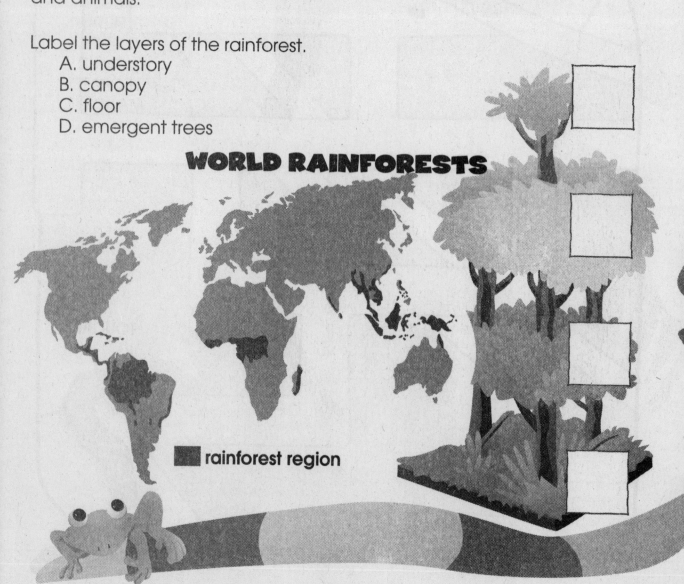

WORLD RAINFORESTS

■ rainforest region

66

©School Zone Publishing Company 12501

A **toucan** uses its colorful bill like a flag to communicate with other toucans. The large bill looks heavy, but it is actually hollow and very light.

Since the rainforest is usually dark, orchids often develop bright flowers and strong scents to attract insects. Some orchids smell like sweet perfume, and others smell like rotting meat.

CAPYBARA
COBRA
CUSCUS
ELEPHANT
GORILLA
LEMUR
LEOPARD
MANDRILL
MARMOSET
OKAPI
ORANGUTAN
PARROT
SCORPION
SLOTH
TAMARIN
TAPIR
TARSIER
TITI
TOUCAN

SEE GLOSSARY · SEE GLOSSARY

```
T W
O L R        H M O T
H Y E C A P Y B A R A
E M A R M O S E T N A R
T L L G O U Y U R D N S Y
V A E F O P R L T R G I J
G O J P P A R R O T I U E W
H N K S I H U I H U L T R L
T O U C A N R A C L N L A I K
F S C O R P I O N J L O N S
K R L C X M I C G T F A I B
E L E O P A R D P O K L R
H V B T A M A R I N M M
N J R Y H C U S C U S
G A      G R
```

A typical rainforest **gecko** has tiny scales and hairs on its feet for a good grip. It can run upside down on branches. If an enemy grabs a gecko's tail, the tail will break off. The gecko can grow a new one later.

©School Zone Publishing Company 12501

Connect the dots from **1** to **15**.
Color the picture.

68

©School Zone Publishing Company 12501

A SWEET TREAT

Help the baker put the cookies in the box.

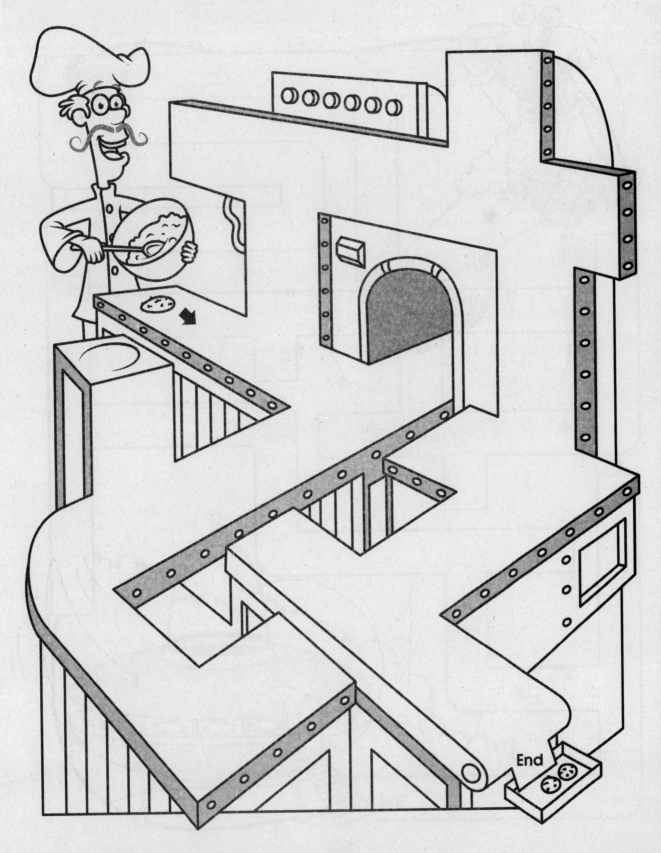

End

©School Zone Publishing Company 12501

JUST VISITING

Help the alien get back to the spaceship.

End

©School Zone Publishing Company 12501

Connect the dots from 1 to 15.
Color the picture.

©School Zone Publishing Company 12501

71

AMAZING ANIMALS

More than a million different kinds of animals have been studied and named so far. Scientists believe there may be several million more types of animals that are still undiscovered. Animals live all over the world—in harsh deserts, the frozen Arctic, dark rainforests, and the bottom of oceans. All animals move, breathe, feed, grow, have young, and adapt to their environment.

Animals are many shapes, colors, and sizes. Even common animals and insects have unique characteristics and behaviors. Some of the most amazing animals are easily recognized by their appearance or abilities. Every animal has developed a special coloring, strength, or defense that makes it able to survive in its habitat.

Each of a chameleon's eyes can look in different directions. Its tongue shoots out so quickly that it can hardly be seen by humans.

CHAMELEON
CHEETAH
FLEA
GIRAFFE
HOWLER
MONKEY
KING COBRA
MAYFLY
OSTRICH
PARROT
PIRANHA
PLATYPUS
QUETZAL
SKUNK
TUATARA

SEE GLOSSARY

```
            S A
          B R V W
        A Z Q K M A Y F L Y C T J C
        D O F U B J N O M D B H T D T Z
        A E E S E T H C H E E T A H B W E A
        Q F H X F T H T K Q N F S M W F N C T L
        G U A O G Z R G B K U T R E L G Q P S T
        P V H M W A H I S R E T Z L S T H L R H
        I D T B O L N X C I R K T E H Y D A J O I
        H J P N U G Q E K J H O Q Y O I N Z T P J G
        L V K I S A H U R T B K G T N K C W Y K H L
        J P A R R O T L M M V K L I X B L C P J L N
        L W M V T A M A G T O I B U R M S K U N K
        N B R O P N H R K L N D N Y A T H S N C
        U W S F O H H K A N G K O D W F T F O
        T D O L P W A L V C F E P R S F P J
        T K Q E U J U P O I H Y Q K T E
        K X R A T Y R B M R P L R
          I F H H S R H S T O
            F T A
```

72

Answer each clue with an animal name from the pictures below.

1. **Smart Talker**
   I can be taught to speak words. _____

2. **Fast Feet**
   I run up to 70 miles per hour. _____

3. **Tall Tail**
   My tail feathers are more than twice my body length. _____

4. **Big Bird**
   I can grow up to 9 feet tall and weigh 300 pounds. _____

5. **Ferocious Fish**
   I attack any creature in the water. _____

6. **Super Leaper**
   I can jump about 200 times my own length. _____

7. **Loud Mouth**
   My call can be heard 3 miles away. _____

8. **A Ton of Tongue**
   My tongue can be longer than the length of my body. _____

9. **Unique Mammal**
   I lay eggs instead of live young. _____

parrot

flea

howler monkey

quetzal

cheetah

chameleon

piranha

ostrich

platypus

©School Zone Publishing Company 12501

DINOSAURS

Dinosaurs were as varied in appearance and habits as land animals are today. Some were huge, and some were tiny. Some walked on two feet, some walked on four feet, some flew, and some swam in the oceans. Some ate plants, and some ate meat. Some had smooth skin, some had scales, and others had bony plates.

Although dinosaurs became extinct 65 million years ago, they resembled modern reptiles in some ways. Some dinosaurs had teeth, skin, and brains similar to those of reptiles living today. There are some big differences between dinosaurs and modern reptiles. Most dinosaurs were enormous, some as large as 190 feet long. Plus, many dinosaurs could walk on two legs, like us.

```
                              T B O H
                              C C O I C
      R T Y R A N N O S A U R U S N D
      S Y U E E A J E X T I N C T R J E K
      X F A T H P O Y F P F O S S I L G S
   F Q R T P X F Y T R I C E R A T O P S
   M V L O S A F R W S I A T L O T J X T I
   P A L E O N T O L O G Y L P S L R Q N
   B R A C H I O S A U R U S E T Y U
 D E V U A B R S H J Y I N C T K O
 L S T E G O S A U R U S B I           R
 G A L L O S A U R U S M
 N I U Y O E N R H Y R
 H A D R O S A U R W
           V S O N
           J R
```

The allosaurus was a meat-eating dinosaur. It had many teeth with saw-like edges.

ALLOSAURUS
APATOSAURUS
BONES
BRACHIOSAURUS
EORAPTOR
EXTINCT
FOSSIL
HADROSAUR
PALEONTOLOGY
REPTILE
STEGOSAURUS
TRICERATOPS
TYRANNOSAURUS

SEE GLOSSARY

©School Zone Publishing Company 12501

IN THE BARNYARD

Find and circle the hidden pictures.

butterfly   mailbox   vase   teapot   TV   shovel   pear   seashell

©School Zone Publishing Company 12501

NOT IN A HURRY

Help Tommy Turtle get to the pond.

End

©School Zone Publishing Company 12501

ON YOUR FEET

The earliest shoe was probably made of hide or braided grass held on the foot by leather cords. In colder climates, people wore moccasins. They were a bag-like covering over the foot tied with string.

Modern shoemaking began in the late 1800s, when machines were used to make shoes. Despite new techniques and materials, many shoe styles have been worn for centuries. Some people in the Netherlands wear wooden shoes. Many people in Asia wear silk slippers. In some places, sandals are the most practical footwear.

Think About It!

Which is more important to you, a shoe's style or its comfort? Why?

```
          P T C S Y
        L B U B L H K
      G H O S M I E L C
    N O I J A H P Y A N
    E S G E N F P S F T C
    M R H V D T E N N I S
    C H B C A G R R G D E
    O S U T L Z S H S V C
    Z T I S O G Y N X
    W T E J B G H O D
    T O V E A K S W F
    A N O B L C L S J
    P K M D L T A H
    T S K N G E W O O
    B H N T W T N H E
    M O C C A S I N S
      E O F Q L K Q
      S M T S J D
        G R S C
```

BALLET
BOOTS
CLEATS
CLOGS
HIGH BUTTON
LOAFERS

MOCCASINS
PUMPS
SANDALS
SLIPPERS
SNOWSHOES
STEEL TOE

TAP SHOES
TENNIS
WOODEN

• SEE GLOSSARY •

A pair of very expensive shoes were made in 1977 for Emperor Bokassa of the Central African Empire (now called the Central African Republic). The shoes cost $85,000 and were covered with pearls.

©School Zone Publishing Company 12501

VEGGIES

A vegetable is a food that comes from a plant's bulb, flower, fruit, leaf, root, seed, or stem. Most vegetables do not have many calories but supply important vitamins and minerals. They are eaten raw or cooked, and they are used as seasoning.

Vegetable plants are different from fruit plants. All vegetables grow from seeds in one season and are replanted the next year. Fruit plants bear fruit for a number of years. Vegetables grow on soft stems or vines. Fruits grow on wood-like stems, trees, or bushes.

Both vegetable plants and fruit plants can produce fruit. A fruit develops from a flower and contains seeds. Tomatoes and watermelons are fruits from vegetable plants.

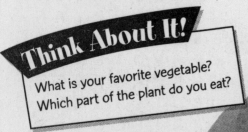

Think About It!

What is your favorite vegetable?
Which part of the plant do you eat?

ASPARAGUS
AVOCADO
BEAN
BEET
CABBAGE
CARROT
CAULIFLOWER
CELERY
CORN
CUCUMBER
LEEK
ONION
PEA
PEPPER
POTATO
RADISH
TURNIP
YAM
ZUCCHINI

```
T N A   V A M T     D T N
A R R E M   N T L Q J   B A S Y
B P W O S C X C I T E H K D S T L O
D G O E A V O C A D O F E B F P I F M D
K B R V P R E H B G V J R K E A K B J H
F O M X C B P J Y B L O F A S J R E G E Y K
S X V I S A C E H A X C N B R N A F E X E M
Y T D C R K F U L R G H A K I P W G C H Z Y T
L A I E I N T C L H E I G D V O I U A T U K P
D K M L T G M U F I J N T G R T N S F R C A J
S H P E A M K M V U F C D Y D A N R J C C S M
O I N R F B L B T G D L T I L T D C H O H Z L
X C M Y E C J E M U P S O H X O B I M R I U H
    X A R N W R T B W G N F G S N N A N
    O R C I G N O B E A N K I H I O
    P R D H Y I J W R M N
    W V O H I M P B Z H
    L S H T R K V
    X M O
```

78

©School Zone Publishing Company 12501

Connect the dots from **1** to **15**.

Color the picture.

©School Zone Publishing Company 12501

ONCE UPON A TIME

Many familiar fairy tales and nursery rhymes were made into books in the 1700s. John Newbery, a writer, publisher, and bookseller in England, recognized that children have special interests. He published translations of Mother Goose, first published in France by Charles Perrault. During Perrault's time, many authors thought that writing books for children was not dignified.

Since then, many fables and stories have been made into books. Find them at the library, and read them for yourself!

Think About It!
Draw a picture of a scene from your favorite story.

```
        T A
      Y P V C C N B
    P P I E D P I P E R V
  G U T D T S F K N I S L U D
  R I S T H E L E S T D N K W H E
  A S F D R E T R P S E O D H L
  B I K G R E T J R G L R C I G
  H N R F A P E D O P S H E C L
  I B V T B I S L B U X A W L H I
  O P D B N U G I J Y N H Y L I P
  O K E I G L A N T C S I K M A O
  T J L T B Y X H S T E N K G W V
  S B M T E H F O V M L R P O B M
  L T G A R G O Y U A E N L H S N
  H E S U I P D X B N A P D T R S
  W P T K P A V N D W C I P L T
  Q W Y T M C N T G O J L G I
  R O H X R B R D R Z C O R S
    C S I T G S F E A S C T
    S N O W W H I T E R K
    X B R V T N U E M I S
        L N V J L
```

CINDERELLA
GOLDILOCKS
HANSEL AND GRETEL
PETER PAN
PETER RABBIT
PIED PIPER
PINOCCHIO
PUSS IN BOOTS
ROBIN HOOD
SLEEPING BEAUTY
SNOW WHITE
THREE LITTLE PIGS

SEE GLOSSARY

80

©School Zone Publishing Company 12501

Answer each clue with a story from the word search.

1. My nose grew if I told a lie. _____

2. I robbed the rich and gave to the poor. _____

3. My carriage turned into a pumpkin. _____

4. I took a bite of a poisoned apple. _____

5. We made our houses of different materials. _____

6. I was chased out of Mr. McGregor's garden. _____

7. We found a gingerbread house. _____

8. I tried to find what was just right. _____

9. I'm the boy who wouldn't grow up. _____

10. I pricked my finger on a spinning wheel. _____

11. I used my pipe to lead rats from town. _____

12. I found a fortune and a royal wife for my master. _____

©School Zone Publishing Company 12501

BEST FRIENDS

For thousands of years, people have kept animals as pets. The most common pets are dogs, cats, fish, birds, reptiles, and hamsters. Many pets can perform work for people. Dogs can keep watch, and cats can control rodents. Some people raise livestock, such as cows, lambs, goats, and even pigs, as pets. Most wild animals do not make good pets, and many states regulate the capture and care of these animals.

Think About It!

What would the perfect pet look like? How would it act?

Veterinarians are doctors who treat animals. Veterinarians can work at animal hospitals, animal shelters, zoos, and universities.

```
      Y W Y C K G
    P B R H R D A F L G
    T P A R A K E E T C O H
    W N I U V B S T Y D L C M
    G L E S F H J B L P E D A E
    U G U I N E A P I G V F N F
    P H B V S A L B G T N I A P
    P M A C A W K C S H M S R H
    Y V F M O N K E Y C T H Y I
    K W P B S L O V E B I R D J
    A T U R T L E D N Z J N L
    V M P L C E B W O T P M
      S Y M H O R S E G L
      H W N K V F J B
          A E
```

SEE GLOSSARY

CANARY · LOVEBIRD
CAT · MACAW
DOG · MONKEY
GOLDFISH · MYNA
GUINEA · PARAKEET
PIG · RABBIT
GUPPY · SNAKE
HAMSTER · TURTLE
HORSE

How many of each type of animal are listed in the puzzle?

1. birds _____

2. mammals _____

3. fish _____

4. reptiles _____

82

©School Zone Publishing Company 12501

STAY AWAY!

Help the boy run past the skunk without getting sprayed.

End

©School Zone Publishing Company 12501

Connect the dots from **I** to **I5**.
Color the picture.

84

©School Zone Publishing Company 12501

FRUITY TOOTY

Fruit is the part of a flowering plant that contains the seeds. Fruit plants are perennials, which are plants that live for more than two years without being replanted. Most fruits are juicy, sweet, or tart, and most are enjoyed as desserts.

Fruits are divided into three types according to the climate in which they thrive. Temperate fruits require a cold season every year and include apples, pears, and many berries. Subtropical fruits need warm or mild temperatures at all times. Most citrus fruits are subtropical, including oranges, lemons, and limes. Dates, olives, and figs are also subtropical. Tropical fruits cannot survive even a light frost. They must be in warm climates. Bananas, mangoes, pineapples, and papayas are tropical fruits.

APPLE
APRICOT
BANANA
BLUEBERRY
CHERRY
DATE
FIG
GRAPE
GRAPEFRUIT
LEMON
LIME
MANGO
MELON
OLIVE
ORANGE
PAPAYA
PEACH
PEAR
PINEAPPLE
PLUM
RASPBERRY
STRAWBERRY

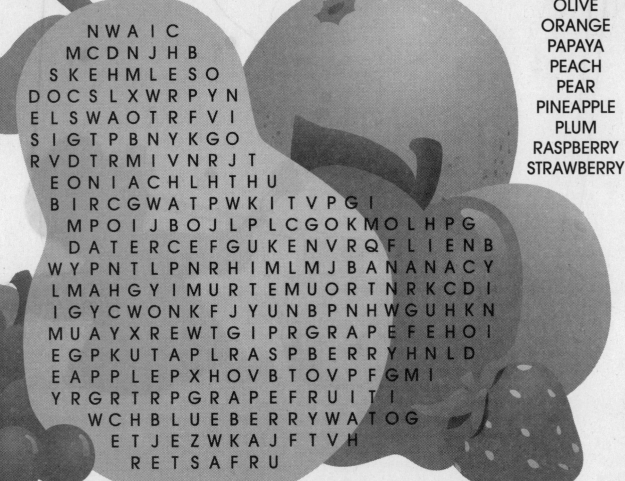

```
      N W A I C
    M C D N J H B
  S K E H M L E S O
D O C S L X W R P Y N
E L S W A O T R F V I
S I G T P B N Y K G O
R V D T R M I V N R J T
  E O N I A C H L H T H U
  B I R C G W A T P W K I T V P G I
  M P O I J B O J L P L C G O K M O L H P G
  D A T E R C E F G U K E N V R Q F L I E N B
W Y P N T L P N R H I M L M J B A N A N A C Y
L M A H G Y I M U R T E M U O R T N R K C D I
I G Y C W O N K F J Y U N B P N H W G U H K N
M U A Y X R E W T G I P R G R A P E F E H O I
E G P K U T A P L R A S P B E R R Y H N L D
E A P P L E P X H O V B T O V P F G M I
Y R G R T R P G R A P E F R U I T I
  W C H B L U E B E R R Y W A T O G
    E T J E Z W K A J F T V H
      R E T S A F R U
```

©School Zone Publishing Company 12501

Connect the dots from **1** to **15**.
Color the picture.

©School Zone Publishing Company 12501

APPLE CORE

Draw a path through the maze.

End

©School Zone Publishing Company 12501

Connect the dots from **1** to **15**.
Color the picture.

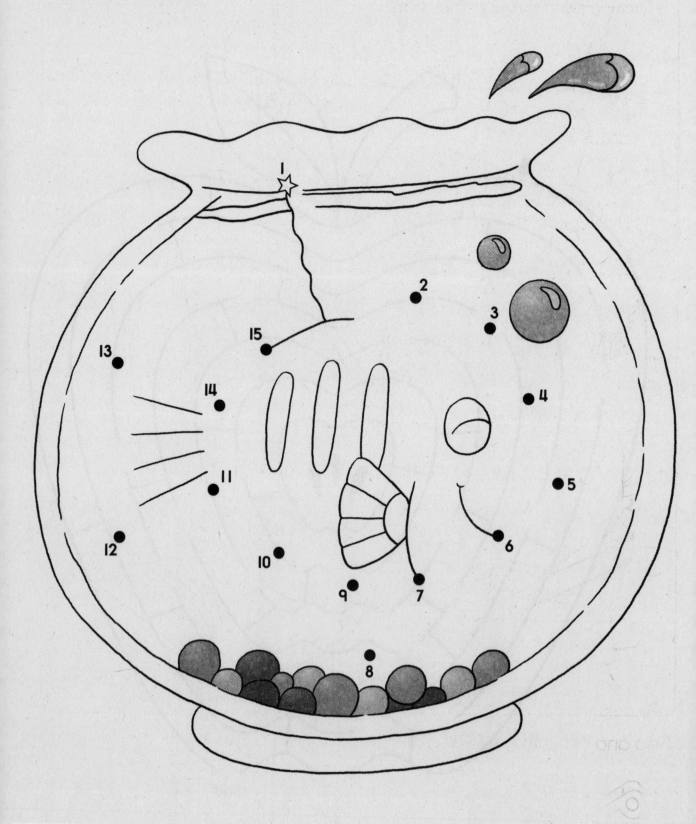

©School Zone Publishing Company 12501

PLAYING IN THE PARK

Find and circle the hidden pictures.

whistle

pie slice

kayak

seashell

pliers

turkey

pinecone

tractor

©School Zone Publishing Company 12501

RUB-A-DUB-DUB!

Find and circle the hidden pictures.

lock

tire

arrow

comb

vitamin

tennis ball

satellite dish

pacifier

©School Zone Publishing Company 12501

TO THE LIBRARY

Help Buzzy Bee return the book on time.

LIBRARY

End

©School Zone Publishing Company 12501

ROOFTOP LANDING

Find and circle the hidden pictures.

couch

cinnamon roll

cheese

boxing glove

juice box

hourglass

cell phone

clover

©School Zone Publishing Company 12501

WELCOME HOME!

Find and circle the hidden pictures.

 clamp

 radio

 tweezers

 collar

 throne

 crate

 wrench

 wreath

©School Zone Publishing Company 12501

Connect the dots from 1 to 15.
Color the picture.

94

©School Zone Publishing Company 12501

LOST AND FOUND

Help the girl find her lost sheep.

End

©School Zone Publishing Company 12501

Connect the dots from **1** to **15**.
Color the picture.

©School Zone Publishing Company 12501

WHALES ON THE GO

Find and circle the hidden pictures.

flamingo   shovel   dragonfly   spider   necktie   coat   lollipop   tulip

©School Zone Publishing Company 12501

BY THE SHORE

Find and circle the hidden pictures.

stocking cap   apple   paintbrush   cookie   broom   bowl   paper clip   spaceship

98

©School Zone Publishing Company 12501

IT'S SNACK TIME!

Help Randy Rhino get to the bananas.

End

©School Zone Publishing Company 12501

AUTHOR TRIVIA

Many books are available for children today. This was not always true. Before 1850, only a few books were written for children. These books were usually based on facts and focused on good manners and polite behavior.

Today, children can read stories from an author's imagination. This kind of story is called fiction.

The names used in this word search are authors of some well-known children's books.

Think About It!

Think about all the books you have read. Which story did you like the most? Which story did you like the least? Why? What book would you recommend to a friend? Why?

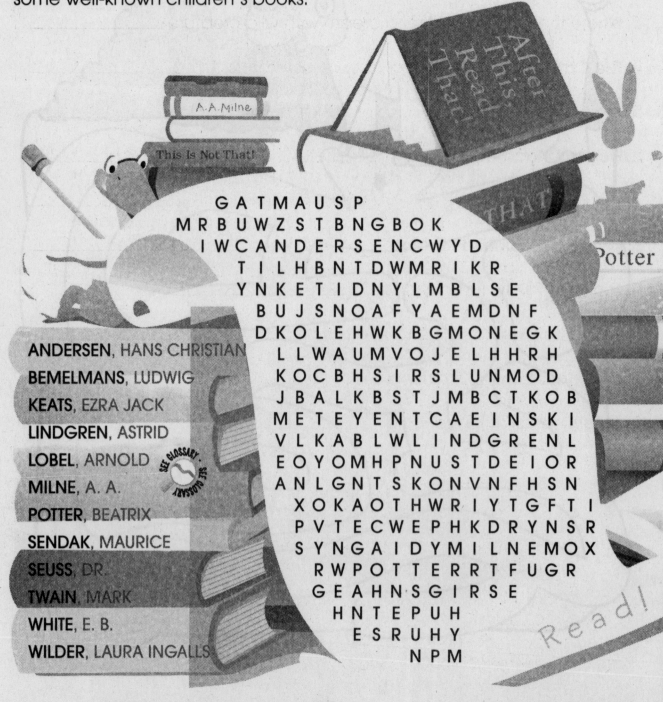

ANDERSEN, HANS CHRISTIAN

BEMELMANS, LUDWIG

KEATS, EZRA JACK

LINDGREN, ASTRID

LOBEL, ARNOLD

MILNE, A. A.

POTTER, BEATRIX

SENDAK, MAURICE

SEUSS, DR.

TWAIN, MARK

WHITE, E. B.

WILDER, LAURA INGALLS

```
    G A T M A U S P
  M R B U W Z S T B N G B O K
    I W C A N D E R S E N C W Y D
    T I L H B N T D W M R I K R
    Y N K E T I D N Y L M B L S E
    B U J S N O A F Y A E M D N F
    D K O L E H W K B G M O N E G K
    L L W A U M V O J E L H H R H
    K O C B H S I R S L U N M O D
    J B A L K B S T J M B C T K O B
    M E T E Y E N T C A E I N S K I
    V L K A B L W L I N D G R E N L
    E O Y O M H P N U S T D E I O R
    A N L G N T S K O N V N F H S N
    X O K A O T H W R I Y T G F T I
    P V T E C W E P H K D R Y N S R
    S Y N G A I D Y M I L N E M O X
    R W P O T T E R R T F U G R
    G E A H N S G I R S E
    H N T E P U H
    E S R U H Y
    N P M
```

100

©School Zone Publishing Company 12501

Answer each clue with an author from the word search.

Check the answers below to see how many you answered correctly.

Then read what your score means on the scorecard.

1. **The Tale of Peter Rabbit**: a raider in McGregor's garden _____

2. **The Adventures of Tom Sawyer**: Huck's best friend _____

3. **Where the Wild Things Are**: a dream with wild creature _____

4. **The Cat in the Hat**: a cat brings rainy day fun _____

5. **The Ugly Duckling**: a sad bird grows into a swan _____

6. **Frog and Toad Are Friends**: the search for a button _____

7. **Pippi Longstocking**: a girl with a pet monkey _____

8. **Winnie-the-Pooh**: a favorite stuffed animal _____

9. **The Snowy Day**: fun in winter _____

10. **Charlotte's Web**: a spider and a pig on a farm _____

11. **Little House on the Prairie**: pioneer life _____

12. **Madeline**: a French schoolgirl _____

SCORECARD

12	8–11	4–7	0–3
Perfect score!	Great Job!	Good try!	Keep reading!

1. Potter 2. Twain 3. Sendak 4. Seuss 5. Andersen 6. Lobel 7. Lindgren 8. Milne 9. Keats 10. White 11. Wilder 12. Bemelmans

©School Zone Publishing Company 12501

Connect the dots from **1** to **15**.
Color the picture.

©School Zone Publishing Company 12501

Help the cuckoo bird fly back to his house.

End

©School Zone Publishing Company 12501

103

AROUND AND AROUND YOU GO!

Draw a path through the maze.

End

©School Zone Publishing Company 12501

Connect the dots from **1** to **15**.

Color the picture.

©School Zone Publishing Company 12501

PLAYING THE BANJO

Find and circle the hidden pictures.

fish   cork   pacifier   sweet potato   candy   spoon   iron   shoe

©School Zone Publishing Company 12501

Find and circle the hidden pictures.

hat　　hammer　　safety cone　　clothes pin　　cheese　　necktie　　saw　　worm

©School Zone Publishing Company 12501

STRIPES ARE IN!

Find and circle the hidden pictures.

pincushion   pepper   palette   toaster   bandage   cane   lighthouse   pillow

©School Zone Publishing Company 12501

FOLLOW THE MAZE

Draw a path through the maze.

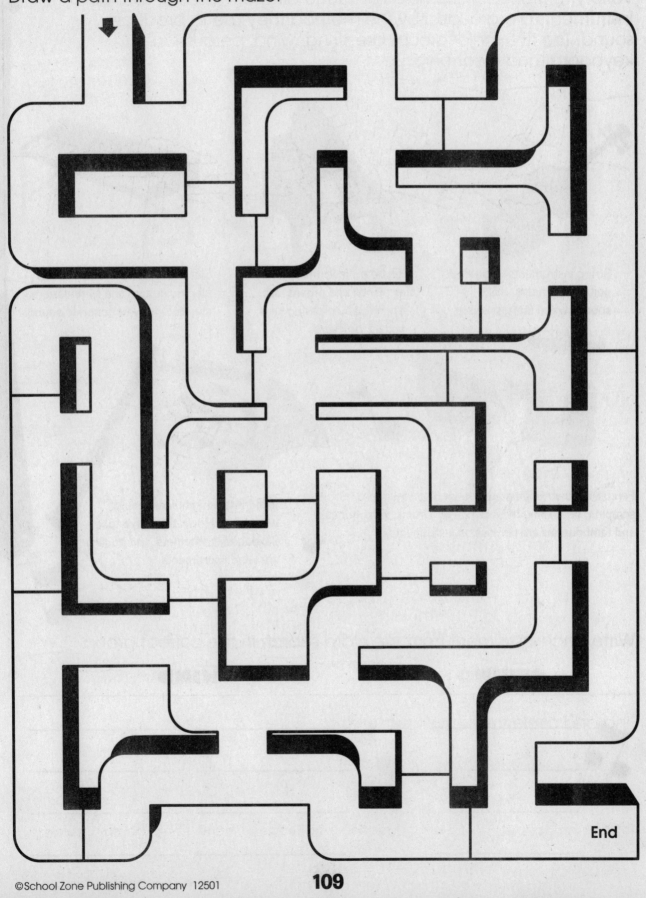

End

©School Zone Publishing Company 12501

MUSICAL INSTRUMENTS

The earliest music was probably created by voices. Now a wide variety of musical instruments produce different kinds of sounds. Instruments are grouped by the method they use to produce sound. The five major groups are string, wind, percussion, keyboard, and electronic.

String instruments, including guitars and harps, make sounds when strings vibrate.

Keyboard instruments, such as pianos and organs, are operated by pressing keys, pedals, or levers.

Electronic instruments, such as electric guitars and synthesizers, use electricity to generate sound.

Percussion instruments are sounded by striking, scraping, or shaking the instrument. Drums, xylophones, and tambourines are percussion instruments.

Wind instruments make music when air is blown through a tube. Saxophones, clarinets, and bugles are wind instruments.

Write each instrument from the word search in the correct group.

STRING

_____   _____

_____   _____

_____   _____

_____   _____

WIND

_____   _____

_____   _____

_____   _____

_____   _____

110

©School Zone Publishing Company 12501

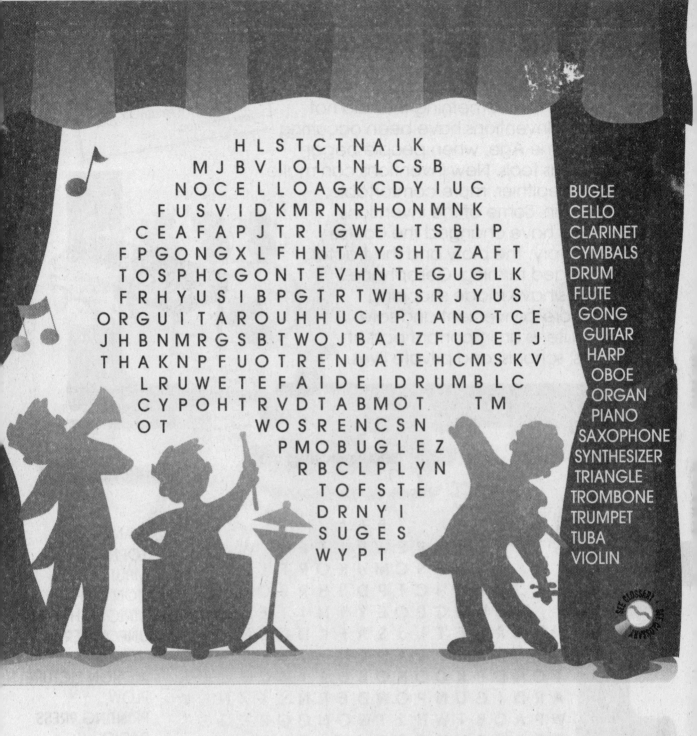

```
        H L S T C T N A I K
      M J B V I O L I N L C S B
    N O C E L L O A G K C D Y I U C
  F U S V I D K M R N R H O N M N K
  C E A F A P J T R I G W E L T S B I P
F P G O N G X L F H N T A Y S H T Z A F T
T O S P H C G O N T E V H N T E G U G L K
F R H Y U S I B P G T R T W H S R J Y U S
O R G U I T A R O U H H U C I P I A N O T C E
J H B N M R G S B T W O J B A L Z F U D E F J
T H A K N P F U O T R E N U A T E H C M S K V
  L R U W E T E F A I D E I D R U M B L C
  C Y P O H T R V D T A B M O T       T M
  O T       W O S R E N C S N
          P M O B U G L E Z
          R B C L P L Y N
          T O F S T E
          D R N Y I
          S U G E S
          W Y P T
```

BUGLE
CELLO
CLARINET
CYMBALS
DRUM
FLUTE
GONG
GUITAR
HARP
OBOE
ORGAN
PIANO
SAXOPHONE
SYNTHESIZER
TRIANGLE
TROMBONE
TRUMPET
TUBA
VIOLIN

PERCUSSION

_____

_____

_____

_____

KEYBOARD AND ELECTRONIC

_____

_____

©School Zone Publishing Company 12501

GADGETS AND GIZMOS

Think About It!

What kind of invention do you need? Draw a picture of your new invention.

Inventing is putting ideas and materials together to make something that did not exist before. Inventions have been occurring since the Stone Age, when people began using rocks as tools. New inventions can make life easier, healthier, more comfortable, and more fun. Some of the inventions listed below have changed the course of world history. The plow and the tractor have changed farming. Cellophane and plastics have made shopping for food more convenient and safe. The computer is an important part of businesses, schools, and private lives.

6. The mice move toward pleasant thoughts of cheese.

5. The light turns on, surprising the mouse on the treadmill.

4. The cat lifts its head in surprise, hitting the button.

7. The mice go down the out chute!

out chute

unsuspecting cat

3. The gears pull the string that tugs the tail of the unsuspecting cat.

2. The string turns the gears.

1. Spider scares the fly, tipping the seesaw.

Mouse Removal Device

It has been said that necessity is the mother of all invention.

```
        B A A
    T Y P E W R I T E R
    X L J S C M U K O P F L
  D R A H C T P D S H R B O N C
  E T W S C E O E Y I N I T E I O
  K G R B E T L J S A F K N C L M T T
  Y T A I R P L A N E M N T S E Y T E
  T O H D P K O O H O B D E I W C J O L A
  A R D I G U N P O W D E R N S T X N E Y
  W P A O B T W H J T G O N G G R K G G T
  D T S C F N Y A F R H M J P L I J I R L
  E R M O T I O N P I C T U R E C N N A
  G M J I O M E F U P O Y E H L M E P
  X H N V X R A Y O T T J S G I A I H
  R B P O F K T H P C T S H G X R
  A Y L T E L E P H O N E H P
    C O M P U T E R H Y T
      W G T P S R T
```

AIRPLANE
CELLOPHANE
COMPUTER
COTTON GIN
ELECTRIC LIGHT
GUNPOWDER
LASER
MOTION PICTURE
PLOW
PRINTING PRESS
RADIO
STEAM ENGINE
TELEGRAPH
TELEPHONE
TRACTOR
TYPEWRITER
X-RAY

SEE GLOSSARY · SEE GLOSSARY

©School Zone Publishing Company 12501

photography
1826

airplane
1903

compact disc
1976

printing press
about 1440

television
1920s

telephone
1876

Match the inventions with their descriptions.
Write the letters in the boxes.

A. a machine that produces printed material

B. a vehicle that can travel through the air

C. a machine that transmits sound and speech
to a distant place

D. the process of producing images on
light-sensitive paper

E. a round, flat disc that stores data, music,
and other information

F. a device that receives broadcasts of moving
pictures and sound

Thomas Edison was a
great inventor. He held
1,093 U.S. patents for
inventions such as the
phonograph, the
lightbulb, batteries,
and cement.

RIVER RAFTING

Help Donald Dog float to Lazy Lake.

©School Zone Publishing Company 12501

Connect the dots from 1 to 15.
Color the picture.

©School Zone Publishing Company 12501

PERFECT PASTA

Help get the fork to the meatball.

End

©School Zone Publishing Company 12501

Connect the dots from **1** to **15**.

Color the picture.

©School Zone Publishing Company 12501

I SCREAM FOR ICE CREAM!

Help Lucky Lemur get to the ice cream.

End

©School Zone Publishing Company 12501

PITCHING THE TENT

Find and circle the hidden pictures.

panda

chair

candy cane

canoe

paper airplane

calculator

balloon

porcupine

119

©School Zone Publishing Company 12501

GAMES AND TOYS

Games and toys aren't just for fun! Games are an important way to teach social skills, such as sharing, teamwork, and sportsmanship. Toys can help develop one's coordination, problem-solving skills, and memory.

Games and toys have entertained people since prehistoric times. In ancient Egypt, some children played with wooden dolls with movable joints and crocodiles with moving jaws. Ancient Roman children played with tops, hoops, and carts. During the Middle Ages, toy horses and soldiers were popular. Today, computers create sophisticated versions of games and toys.

Think About It!

What games and toys did you play with when you were younger? What are your favorite games and toys now?

SEE GLOSSARY · SEE GLOSSARY

```
          J L I X O
        T W V E A J A C K S
      H B C S R B Y N D Z V R C
    W N Z O P D Z R A F P S Z H T S
      I E S O F S E Z E L O K X D R E C
    P V F H K T R A M P O L I N E I J F H
  E A U D T U A D G M I K G O H T C A R G
  J H R Z A Y O T K Y L D O L O H Y F D T A
  F G O Z W P H E O N C T B Y N C B T B I
  Z C K L S N J B M Y H R V F L G J O G
  P U P P E T A H O J D E G H E B       P
  H F T H W E R T S A T O S L T N
  T C R A Y O N M D B R R L S M O
  T B S F C O U Z Z O A N D V Z N
  Z O A O G Y P O B L O C K O W T N
  P Z L T O X Y P L Y       R P V
  D P Q L M G H O N       Z L E
      E T
```

BALL
BALLOON
BLOCK
BOOK
CAR
CHESS
CRAYON
DOLL
JACKS
PUPPET
PUZZLE
SKATEBOARD
TOP
TRAMPOLINE
TRICYCLE
YO-YO

©School Zone Publishing Company 12501

POND HOP

Help Freddie Frog hop to the lily pad on the other side of the pond.

End

©School Zone Publishing Company 12501

Connect the dots from 1 to 20.
Color the picture.

122

©School Zone Publishing Company 12501

SPORTS

Sports are activities played for fun, exercise, or competition. Many people participate in amateur sports, from backyard games of badminton to organized softball leagues. Professional athletes participate in sports as careers.

There are different types of sports. Individual sports do not require a group or team of players. Combative sports set one person against another, as in boxing or wrestling. Water sports include fishing, swimming, and water polo. Outdoor sports involve people in nature and include camping, hiking, and orienteering. Team sports, such as baseball and basketball, require players to communicate and work together.

ARCHERY	GOLF	POLO
BASEBALL	GYMNASTICS	SKATEBOARDING
BASKETBALL	HOCKEY	SNOWBOARDING
BOCCIE	IN-LINE SKATING	SOCCER
BOWLING	JUDO	SQUASH
CROQUET	LUGE	TENNIS
FOOTBALL	MOUNTAIN BIKING	VOLLEYBALL

```
        Y H J A T
      T B A S K E T B A L L
    G W G C R T S B O V I C G
    H S S N O W B O A R D I N G D
  S L Q K A R L E C T T E N N I S
  F K U P R G U F C H M V O F K T L
P R I A B C W H S E G O N J O P B T
H O N S T H B O B R S U K T O N O E
H V L H W E T O G Y M N A S T I C S
O O I O B R B S W N H T Y O B J C B
C L N L V Y H O J L Q A K L A K I P
K L E Q U N Z L A C I I F C L W E
E E S S R G V T K R M N Q B L
Y Y K F N M E W O O D B G U
T O B A S E B A L L Q Y I T E L
P S A T P H W I O P U V K N C P
Y B L I G R K N Q L E G I Q G
R L N C J U D O S T R N G
  S G M   N G O P T G
```

SEE GLOSSARY · SEE GLOSSARY

©School Zone Publishing Company 12501

FOURTEEN LARGEST U.S. CITIES

Most cities began at sites that were protected from enemy attacks. Over time, people settled in cities that were along trade routes, most often located by rivers.

Cities grew as new methods of transportation, such as boats, canals, roads, and railways, made it possible to ship raw materials.

Farming methods improved, providing food for more people. Jobs opened up during the Industrial Revolution, and large cities evolved.

Think About It!

What are some advantages of living in a big city? What are some disadvantages?

CHICAGO
DALLAS
DETROIT
HOUSTON
INDIANAPOLIS
JACKSONVILLE
LOS ANGELES

NEW YORK
PHILADELPHIA
PHOENIX
SAN ANTONIO
SAN DIEGO
SAN FRANCISCO
SAN JOSE

New York was the largest US city in 1900 and 2012.

Population of New York
1900: 3,437,202
2012: 8,336,697

```
Y  D P I                                              S
                                                     A T
O R A H X H E I G                                    R Y
D S L O D E T R O I T D O P      O D        S T D
S I A E A C N L S O L H A J C S      C        A X Y
P F A S N H N H T M A X V I L A K    S H   A N J F
G H I N I F G T I G G N N G G L G    M L   Q J A
S U I N X W R H O C H H E S A N A N T O N I O C
T H P L D A L A B N A I W Y P I L S I S O N S R
J S O Y A I G H N E X G Y O L S V T O A V J E N
A N U T D A J A C K S O N V I L L E N L I C D
N C F S D E N D E I T R I R L G S T G K H L
 J D M T Y L A O T S K J S A N D I E G O M
  O N N O L P P Y K C V B N J W K L J N
   O X N O H O X R O N A T O C E T L
    D I L M C D P N L S S R C
     E T A I X F  Y I        S P
      R S                    N I
       S                     N I
```

©School Zone Publishing Company 12501

AFTERNOON DIP

Find and circle the hidden pictures.

pitcher   locket   clownfish   blimp   cannon   squid   atom   hook

©School Zone Publishing Company 12501

HANGING AROUND

Help Sammy Snake find his glasses.

End

©School Zone Publishing Company 12501

Connect the dots from **1** to **15**.
Color the picture.

Connect the dots from **1** to **15**.

Color the picture.

©School Zone Publishing Company 12501

HAWAII THE ALOHA STATE

Hawaii is a chain of 132 islands in the Pacific Ocean. It is the only U.S. state that does not lie on the mainland of North America. Volcanoes, some of which are still active, formed the islands. Hawaii's natural beauty and pleasant climate make it a popular vacation destination.

The original settlers were from Polynesia, but today Hawaii is home to people of many ethnic and national backgrounds. The Hawaiian customs of friendliness and vivacity give it the nickname "Aloha State." The word aloha means "greetings" or "love" in the Hawaiian language. Vacationers are often greeted with a wreath of flowers called a lei (la) when they arrive at a Hawaiian island.

BANANAS
CANYONS
HONOLULU
HULA
ISLANDS
KAUAI
LAVA
LEIS
MAUI
MOUNTAINS
OAHU
PAPAYAS
PEARL HARBOR
PINEAPPLES
POLYNESIANS
SUGAR
VALLEYS
VOLCANOES
WAVES

The Hawaiian alphabet has only 12 letters — a, e, h, i, k, l, m, n, o, p, u, and w.

```
              B
       L         A K
       O         U O
       I A     L O Y
 H B     U V H I Y       Y J
 V G L U A   G M A U I   B T D G
   A C M N W V A L L E Y S
   V O L C A N O E S I
   A A P T N V I U
   G Y O K T R E H
 H I L I S L A N D S W L
 F M S N D M G U I R C M
 N K Y O D T N P P A X N K S
 U I H O V U L E I S A I A P O
 X A O P P L N V N U P P G O H P
 T U N F Y A L T E M B L A L I O
 V M O B A N A N A S A R N Y C L
 A S L E Y M X S P I U I S N A Y G
 L Y U U E L T K P O N T W E N S M
 U R L G I S H U L A U S M S Y U
 F U V A V W A E R O V L I O I
 L C O S R E I S B R Y Y A N W
   P E A R L H A R B O R N S
   E N R P T N S N Y S
```

©School Zone Publishing Company 12501

129

Connect the dots from **1** to **20**.

Color the picture.

©School Zone Publishing Company 12501

DINOSAUR GAMES

Help Donna Dinosaur find her babies.

End

©School Zone Publishing Company 12501

DINOSAUR MINIATURE GOLF

Find and circle the hidden pictures.

apple   chair   tulip   bee   bird   barrel   hat   boot

132

©School Zone Publishing Company 12501

Find and circle the hidden pictures.

necktie

palette

pie slice

horn

cowboy
hat

diamond

jelly
bean

mushroom

PAINTED PINK

Help Fiona Flamingo get to the paint.

End

©School Zone Publishing Company 12501

Connect the dots from **1** to **20**.
Color the picture.

#1 FANS

Find and circle the hidden pictures.

olive   peas   birthday cake   fishing pole   starfish   jet   inner tube   windmill

©School Zone Publishing Company 12501

Connect the dots from **1** to **20**.
Color the picture.

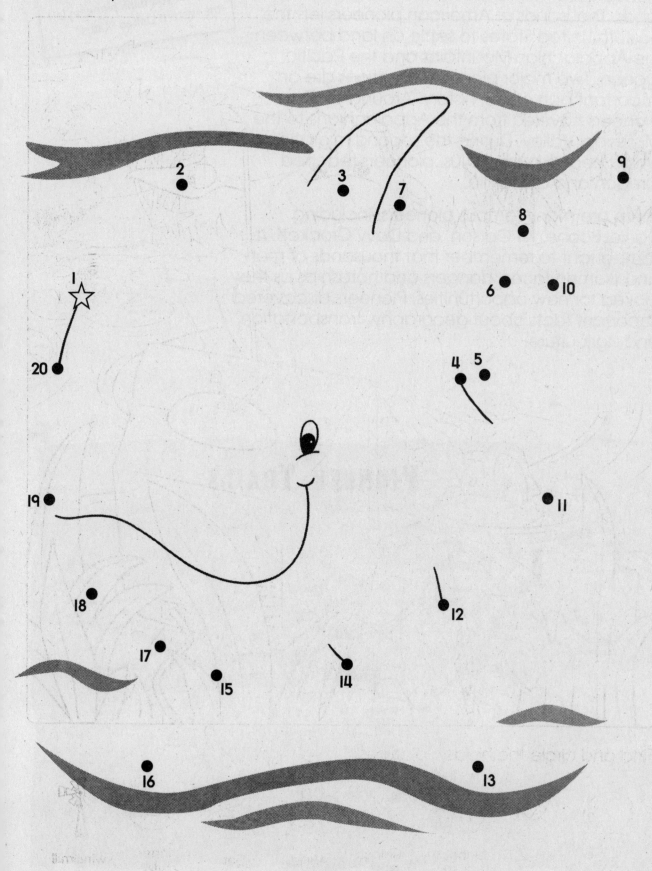

©School Zone Publishing Company 12501

PIONEERS

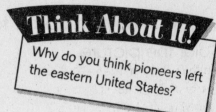

Think About It!

Why do you think pioneers left the eastern United States?

Pioneers are the first people to venture into new lands. Thousands of American pioneers left the eastern United States to settle on land between the Appalachian Mountains and the Pacific Ocean. Two major pioneer migrations are an important part of U.S. history. Around 1760, pioneers traveled from the Appalachians to the Mississippi Valley. During the second migration, which began in the 1840s, pioneers reached Oregon and California.

There are many famous pioneers, including Daniel Boone, Kit Carson, and Davy Crockett. It is important to remember that thousands of men and women faced dangers and hardships as they looked for new opportunities. Pioneers discovered important facts about geography, transportation, and agriculture.

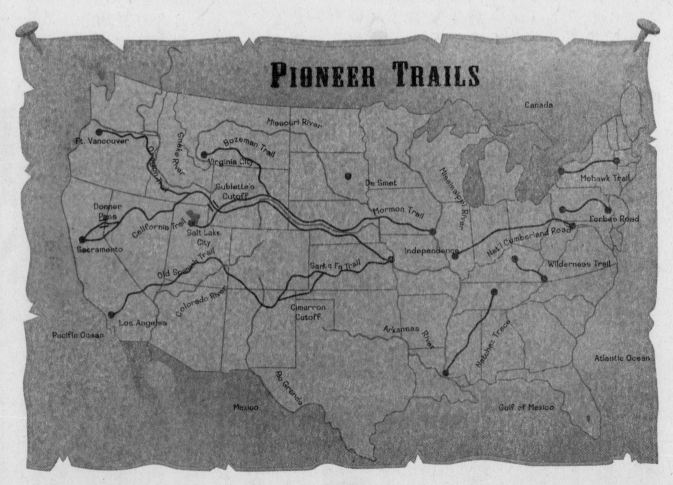

PIONEER TRAILS

138

©School Zone Publishing Company 12501

In the winter of 1846–1847, a party of 82 pioneers became snowbound at Donner Pass, a cut through the Sierra Nevadas. Through their desperate measures, 47 people survived.

Laura Ingalls Wilder wrote eight "Little House" books based on her pioneer childhood. Five of the stories take place in De Smet, South Dakota.

Conestoga wagons are named for the Conestoga River in Pennsylvania, where they were first built in the early 1700s. These covered wagons were used by many pioneers.

```
T E       G H S              A P L E       D T S
A E M D V Q M R P I D X S C R W R E Y F D J B P C M V P G
H P J S F D N V Y B O W I E R D O S Q D S E O N H C W S C
J F P D S U B L E T T E K I C O L T E R R M O T L L N D
E C L R E C L A R K X A Y O N C P G C E I N R Y O E E
T B F E I K A W I V G J K H N F K L N L S E B S U B W
M D W T S T F R F E B S G W E G S E Y H O Y Q T G O G
T R U K E T H S N E H M D R C P W T E N W H A H I
O N S T S E K I O R L E I F W P I R T J I Y L L W
V P K H K M D M J N E Y L T M B S I X O N H R I T
P Y S N B R I D G E R W E H L R W H I T M A N
```

SEE GLOSSARY · SEE GLOSSARY

APPLESEED, JOHNNY
BOONE, DANIEL
BOWIE, JAMES
BRIDGER, JIM
CARSON, KIT
CLARK, WILLIAM
COLTER, JOHN
CROCKETT, DAVY

DONNER, GEORGE & JACOB
JEMISON, MARY
LEWIS, MERIWETHER
MCLOUGHLIN, JOHN
SMITH, JEBEDIAH
SUBLETTE, WILLIAM
WHITMAN, MARCUS

©School Zone Publishing Company 12501

GARBAGE PICKER

Help Rita Raccoon get to the garbage can.

End

©School Zone Publishing Company 12501

ELEPHANT EXPLORER

Find and circle the hidden pictures.

pants   saw   pail   leaf   sailboat   spatula   crown   headphones

©School Zone Publishing Company 12501

TRAILBLAZER

Help Billy Beetle find the house on the lake.

©School Zone Publishing Company 12501

Connect the dots from **1** to **20**.
Color the picture.

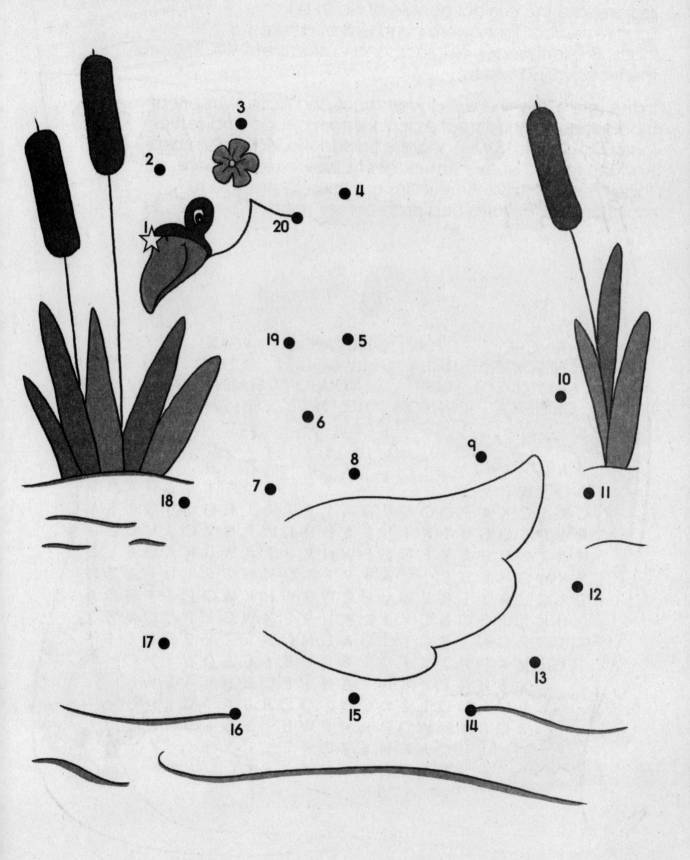

©School Zone Publishing Company 12501

NATIVE AMERICANS

Native Americans (often called American Indians) are the original people of North and South America. There were hundreds of different tribes. The languages, religions, and customs of the tribes varied widely.

In the late 1700s, the U.S. government and Native American tribal leaders signed treaties to maintain peace and settle land disputes. In 1830, Congress passed the Indian Removal Act. This forced Native Americans to live on reservations. Today, many Native Americans continue to struggle to maintain their cultures and protect their rights.

Think About It!

How is the life of a modern Native American different from a Native American's life before European settlers arrived?

APACHE   CROW   KICKAPOO   POMO   SIOUX
CHEROKEE   HAIDA   KWAKIUTL   PUEBLO   UTE
CHEYENNE   INUIT   NAVAJO   SEMINOLE
CHIPPEWA   IROQUOIS   NEZ PERCE   SHAWNEE

```
A U                                           T A H E
G O Y W H V J                             I R Z U A P E
C C K I C K A P O O C U W A I P T A I R O Q U O I S Y C
C P W P S O E U T K I U F S H U K W P N V C J V D O D A
H A X I C H E Y E N N E W H V U P A W U H A O A L E
X K W O H R B S I U A I P P A O X U I F I U F V J N
G I Q U R Z L B E W V P C W G W H K W O P T Y G O A
U H X T O O N O Y A M A H R P N W C F P C O L H
T C R O W I N Q Z J O A C N O N E Z P E R C E I
L I V K P R T X E O T P S H E L E E C W Y N O
O K E H N P P K W Y A N I E O B H K A E W N
S E M I N O L E D C O L O C B U A L C L
Z O C I M W O P H P K W U T E O P U
I U O A C H E R O K E E U X I
O K F X R J C K I P O
```

SEE GLOSSARY · SEE GLOSSARY

144

©School Zone Publishing Company 12501

Northwestern totem poles serve as an emblem of a family or clan. They can tell a story or mark a grave.

Inuit live farther north than any other people. The Inuit obtain most of their food from hunting and fishing.

Hiawatha, an Iroquois leader, helped bring peace to the five main Iroquois tribes. They formed an alliance called the Great Peace, also known as the Iroquois League.

Buffalo provided meat, clothing, and shelter for Native Americans living on the Plains.

Little Big Horn
•Montana
  •Wounded
  Knee
  South Dakota

•Serpent
Mound
Ohio

Sequoyah invented a system of writing for his native language of Cherokee.

•Mesa Verde
Colorado

Trail of Tears
to Oklahoma

Sacagawea, a Shoshone woman, was a guide and interpreter for the Lewis and Clark expedition to the Pacific Ocean.

Southwestern Pueblo people lived in connected stone or adobe buildings that were up to four stories tall.

Crazy Horse, Geronimo, Osceola, and Pontiac were famous Native Americans.

©School Zone Publishing Company 12501

FLYING HOME

Help Betty Bird fly to her tree.

End

©School Zone Publishing Company 12501

Connect the dots from 1 to 20.
Color the picture.

©School Zone Publishing Company 12501

CANADA

Canada is the second largest country in the world. It is rich in scenic beauty and natural resources. A federal government binds Canada's ten provinces and three territories in a democratic nation. Canada's closest economic and social ties are with the United States, which shares common interests and a common background.

Think About It!

Why do you think Canada's population is less than the United States' population even though Canada is a larger country?

Approximate Area
Canada 3.84 million square miles
United States 3.79 million square miles

Approximate Population (2013)
Canada   35 million
United States   317 million

On February 15,1965, Canada flew a new flag. It showed a red maple leaf, a symbol of Canada.

United States

Yukon

Northwest Territory

Nunavut

British Columbia

Alberta

Saskatchewan

Manitoba

Hudson Bay

Ontario

Quebec

Newfoundland and Labrador

Prince Edward Island

Nova Scotia

New Brunswick

United States

Niagara Falls

©School Zone Publishing Company 12501

The territory of Nunavut was established in 1999. The word Nunavut means "our land" in Inuit.

Canadians celebrate Canada Day on July 1, the date in 1867 that Canada became a country. Despite its independence, Canada recognizes the British monarch as head of state.

Niagara Falls is one of the greatest hydraulic power sources in the world.

PROVINCES

ALBERTA
BRITISH COLUMBIA
MANITOBA
NEW BRUNSWICK
NEWFOUNDLAND AND LABRADOR
NOVA SCOTIA
ONTARIO
PRINCE EDWARD ISLAND
QUEBEC
SASKATCHEWAN

TERRITORIES

NORTHWEST
NUNAVUT
YUKON

Canada has two official languages, English and French.

Hello! Bonjour!

TALL AND SHORT

Help George Giraffe get to Zeb Zebra.

End

©School Zone Publishing Company 12501

Connect the dots from **1** to **20**.

Color the picture.

©School Zone Publishing Company 12501

EXPLORERS

Since prehistoric times, people have engaged in exploration as they searched for food and shelter. Eventually, prehistoric people populated all of the continents except Antarctica.

During ancient and medieval times, explorers from Europe, the Middle East, and Asia charted territories far from their homelands. Even so, many parts of the world remained isolated until the Europeans became active explorers during a period known as the Age of Exploration, which lasted from the early 15th century until the 17th century. By the early 20th century, most parts of the world had been mapped. New frontiers for exploration still exist deep in the oceans and outer space.

c. 950 - 1000

ERIK THE RED
This Norwegian explorer was named Erik Thorvaldsson. He was nicknamed for his red hair. He named and colonized Greenland.

c. 1540-1595

SIR FRANCIS DRAKE
Drake was the first Englishman to sail around the world. He earned a reputation as a ruthless pirate.

1930 - 2012

NEIL ARMSTRONG
This U.S. astronaut was the first person to step on the moon. He and Edwin Aldrin Jr. landed on the moon on July 20, 1969.

1254 - 1324

MARCO POLO
This Italian explorer became famous for his travels. He wrote about his journey in his book, *The Travels of Marco Polo.*

1491 - 1557

JACQUES CARTIER
When he explored North America, this French explorer became friends with the Iroquois people. He named Canada based on the Huron-Iroquois word "Kanata," which means "village."

152

©School Zone Publishing Company 12501

AMUNDSEN, ROALD
ARMSTRONG, NEIL
CABOT, JOHN
CARTIER, JACQUES
CHAMPLAIN, SAMUEL DE
CLARK, WILLIAM
COLUMBUS, CHRISTOPHER
CORTÉS, HERNANDO
DRAKE, SIR FRANCIS
ERIKSON, LEIF

ERIK THE RED
HILLARY, SIR EDMUND PERCIVAL
HUDSON, HENRY
LEWIS, MERIWETHER
LIVINGSTONE, DAVID
MAGELLAN, FERDINAND
MARQUETTE, JACQUES
POLO, MARCO
PONCE DE LEÓN, JUAN
SOTO, HERNANDO DE

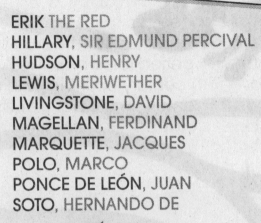

SEE GLOSSARY · SEE GLOSSARY

Jeanne Baré was probably the first woman to sail around the world. In 1766, this young Frenchwoman disguised herself as a male servant and sailed on the first French voyage around the world.

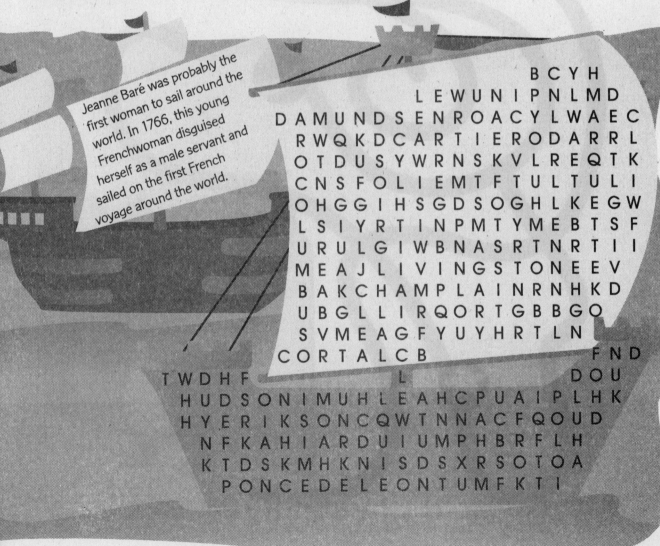

```
                              B C Y H
                      L E W U N I P N L M D
    D A M U N D S E N R O A C Y L W A E C
    R W Q K D C A R T I E R O D A R R L
    O T D U S Y W R N S K V L R E Q T K
    C N S F O L I E M T F T U L T U L I
    O H G G I H S G D S O G H L K E G W
    L S I Y R T I N P M T Y M E B T S F
    U R U L G I W B N A S R T N R T I I
    M E A J L I V I N G S T O N E E V
    B A K C H A M P L A I N R N H K D
    U B G L L I R Q O R T G B B G O
    S V M E A G F Y U Y H R T L N
    C O R T A L C B              F N D
  T W D H F              L          D O U
  H U D S O N I M U H L E A H C P U A I P L H K
  H Y E R I K S O N C Q W T N N A C F Q O U D
  N F K A H I A R D U I U M P H B R F L H
  K T D S K M H K N I S D S X R S O T O A
  P O N C E D E L E O N T U M F K T I
```

HIDE-AND-SEEK

Help Daisy Dog find Buddy Bear.

End

©School Zone Publishing Company 12501

PRACTICE MAKES PERFECT

Find and circle the hidden pictures.

bee   sandwich   ornament   stop sign   bird   tape measure   drum   pinwheel

©School Zone Publishing Company 12501

WHAT A SNACK!

Find and circle the hidden pictures.

fish   cactus   quarter   wooden board   grapes   cabbage   maracas   glasses

156

©School Zone Publishing Company 12501

PECULIAR PALS

Help Rob Raccoon get to Felix Flamingo.

End

SOUTH AMERICA

South America is the fourth largest continent. South America has a wide range of climates, including dry deserts, steamy rainforests, and cold mountain peaks. Most of the continent is warm all year. The exception is high in the Andes Mountains, where it is always cold. The Amazon River Basin supports the world's largest tropical rainforest. The Andes Mountains form the world's largest mountain range. South America is also home to many spectacular resources, landforms, and species.

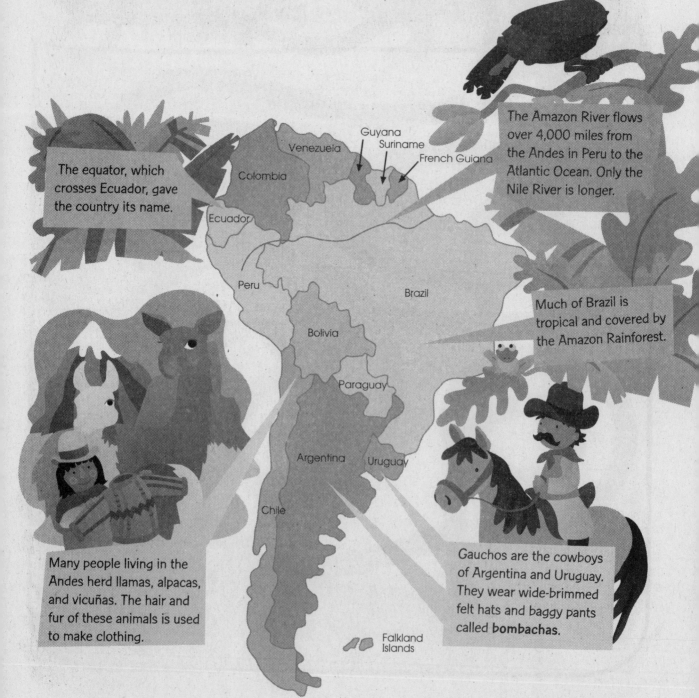

The equator, which crosses Ecuador, gave the country its name.

The Amazon River flows over 4,000 miles from the Andes in Peru to the Atlantic Ocean. Only the Nile River is longer.

Much of Brazil is tropical and covered by the Amazon Rainforest.

Many people living in the Andes herd llamas, alpacas, and vicuñas. The hair and fur of these animals is used to make clothing.

Gauchos are the cowboys of Argentina and Uruguay. They wear wide-brimmed felt hats and baggy pants called **bombachas**.

Venezuela
Guyana
Suriname
French Guiana
Colombia
Ecuador
Peru
Brazil
Bolivia
Paraguay
Argentina
Uruguay
Chile
Falkland Islands

©School Zone Publishing Company 12501

Rainforests surround the Amazon River. The Amazon Rainforest accounts for nearly half of the world's remaining rainforests. Every day, rainforests are cleared for development, causing erosion and endangering animals.

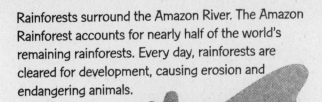

Think About It!

South America has been slow to develop its rich natural resources. Why?

ARGENTINA
BOLIVIA
BRAZIL
CHILE
COLOMBIA
ECUADOR
FALKLAND ISLANDS
FRENCH GUIANA
GUYANA
PARAGUAY
PERU
SURINAME
URUGUAY
VENEZUELA

SEE GLOSSARY · SEE GLOSSARY

```
E C U A D O R V A
F R O D B G C S P
A P Y L M O U U A C
L R Z D O L G Y R L
K T G R E M U L A K Y
V R L U H E C T B Z G N I
Z B G N E A F B G N H Y I U R A K
I S Y R H U N J R Z V T H N A E H L
D C T I U N O Y D E A V B N I F Y C I U
E C H N F L R C D I U Z L E H Z N D L J
B O L I V I A V I K S R I U V N L K A M K
J Y A L Y A N C H N L C L I E A G U A Y
G W F R E N C H G U I A N A V N L U M D
H P G S U Z V A F N D N M S Y M I A N
U H C E O D K E Z I R L D O E V T U R
P D P U R U G U A Y P H S Z H P Y P T
E Y C U B I U Y Z Q H A N Y C B T A Z E
```

©School Zone Publishing Company 12501

Connect the dots from **1** to **20**.
Color the picture.

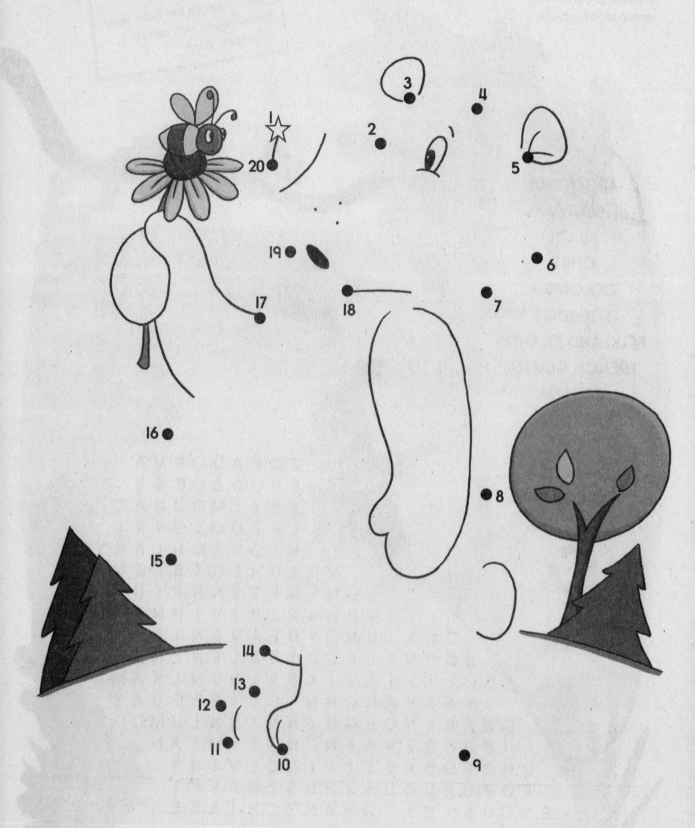

©School Zone Publishing Company 12501

BUILDING A HOME

Help Bertha Beaver get to her home.

End

©School Zone Publishing Company 12501

ALASKA THE LAST FRONTIER

Alaska is the largest state in the United States. It is more than twice the size of Texas. But Alaska has fewer people than any other state.

The United States purchased Alaska from Russia in 1867 for about two cents per acre. At the time, people made fun of the purchase, thinking that Alaska was nothing but snow and ice. The United States soon realized that the value of Alaskan resources was far greater than the purchase price.

Alaska's state flag was designed by Benny Benson, a 13-year-old boy. Seven stars form the Big Dipper, symbolizing strength and the gold mining industry. The eighth star in the corner is the North Star, representing the state's northern location.

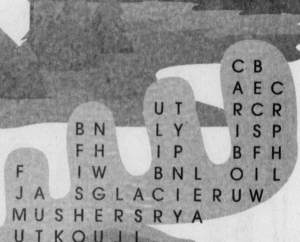

```
S D
E E                                                      C B
H P       C E      Y I                           U T     A E C
Q G J     N A      A K                B N        L Y     R C R
    U H T I M B E R B A     L     F   F H        I P     I S P H
      O U A M I N E R A L S   E R   J A   I W    B N L   B F
              Y W M       U T K O U J L  S G L A C I E R U W
          H M O U N T A I N S T N K M   M U S H E R S R Y A
      K A Y A K Y G Y A G N E N T V O R P D
      J E M I N A N C H O R A G E M H A
          V S K H L G R Y T F R J
          E T D S T W R N
          V A B I H P M J
          D E H L R Q O U U B
          G O R S U I S N R
          V O L C A N O E S
          L I F H K U B A T
          C M U I E I T U K
          V A V K R T I S
            N O A G
```

ANCHORAGE	MINERALS
CARIBOU	MOUNTAINS
EARTHQUAKE	MUSHERS
FISH	OIL
GLACIER	SALMON
GOLD	SEALS
INUIT	TIMBER
JUNEAU	VOLCANOES
KAYAK	

SEE GLOSSARY · SEE GLOSSARY

Think About It!

Design a flag to symbolize your state.

Alaska's most western point is only 51 miles from Russia. Why do you think Russia sold Alaska to the United States?

162

©School Zone Publishing Company 12501

IT'S GOAL TIME!

Help Peter Porcupine get to his soccer ball.

End

BUILDINGS

Buildings are designed by architects to meet goals of use, strength, and beauty. Early people lived in simple huts and tents for protection from the weather and animals. Today's buildings are a diverse and elaborate mixture of styles and purposes. They range from simple homes to temples, monuments, churches, schools, and commercial buildings.

Think About It!

Architects debate about whether the most important focus of building design is the building's form or its function. What is your opinion?

The development of elevators in the 1800s led to the design and construction of skyscrapers.

```
C V E A P T I S W P U C H U R C H
A S Y K Y N P I L B E O T C T
F T O W E R W A Q E L S V I S
I N H D L V A D G W R P G O Y
U A E M J P N M S O E I H C N L S K E
L R K Y X L N K I A D T O D A I V W Y
S H W G C A T H E D R A L V G B D E H
H K T H G N G O R A F L C N O R I R
D I Y U S E F B M T I U H U G A V N
Y V R S V T P Y E H M P A C U R S T
N K E B C A A M T O O S L A E Y N M
R Y T D E R L D O Y G T L S O L C
B R S T M I A E I D O O E T W D G
N A N H E U N P B U E I N L P I A
P L G E O M I S E J M O O E T U
V Y O D U S P M I R U D S P P A
K L N Q C R S L D G S B N M T Y
P T R U H Y U F E A E R V E N
L H O U S E M O S Q U E T M S
A L X M T M L Y P R M Y C E T
V C P R B K P O N S B K T H P
```

CABIN
CASTLE
CATHEDRAL
CHURCH
HOSPITAL
HOTEL
HOUSE
LIBRARY
MOSQUE
MUSEUM
PAGODA
PLANETARIUM
PYRAMID
SKYSCRAPER
STADIUM
SYNAGOGUE
TEMPLE
TOMB
TOWER

©School Zone Publishing Company 12501

AMUSEMENT PARK FUN

Find and circle the hidden pictures.

bug   grapes   book   chest   squirrel   ladder   balloon   television

©School Zone Publishing Company 12501

JUST HANGING AROUND

Find and circle the hidden pictures.

kite   rope   straw   bird bath   wrench   bread   pot of gold   popcorn

©School Zone Publishing Company 12501

AGRICULTURE

Agriculture is the science of growing plants and raising animals for food, clothing, medicines, and other human needs. Agriculture is the world's most important industry. At one time, most people were farmers. As agricultural methods improved, farmers were able to provide a greater number of plants and animals.

Think About It!

What is the major agricultural product in your state? How important is agriculture to your state's economy and identity?

Large, corporate farms meet a great portion of the world's agricultural needs. Smaller, private farms are important to maintain product and food diversity and availability. The main branches of agriculture include crop farming, dairy farming, ranching, poultry raising, and fruit growing.

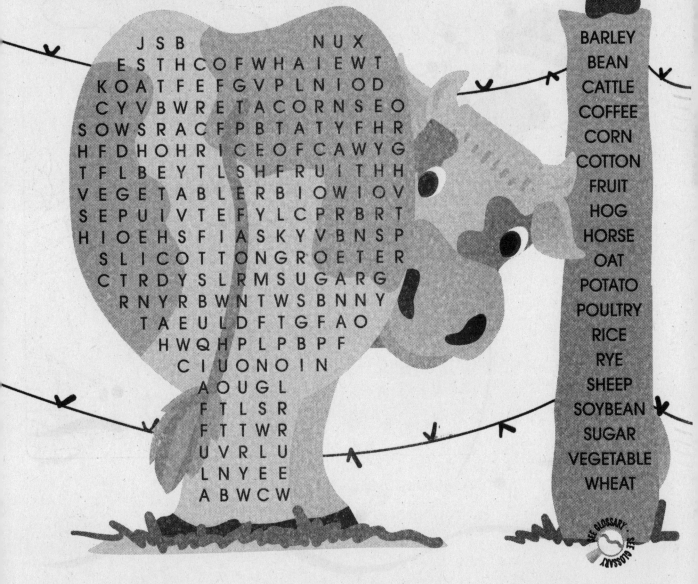

```
        J S B              N U X
      E S T H C O F W H A I E W T
    K O A T F E F G V P L N I O D
    C Y V B W R E T A C O R N S E O
    S O W S R A C F P B T A T Y F H R
    H F D H O H R I C E O F C A W Y G
    T F L B E Y T L S H F R U I T H H
    V E G E T A B L E R B I O W I O V
    S E P U I V T E F Y L C P R B R T
    H I O E H S F I A S K Y V B N S P
    S L I C O T T O N G R O E T E R
    C T R D Y S L R M S U G A R G
      R N Y R B W N T W S B N N Y
      T A E U L D F T G F A O
      H W Q H P L P B P F
      C I U O N O I N
      A O U G L
      F T L S R
      F T T W R
      U V R L U
      L N Y E E
      A B W C W
```

BARLEY
BEAN
CATTLE
COFFEE
CORN
COTTON
FRUIT
HOG
HORSE
OAT
POTATO
POULTRY
RICE
RYE
SHEEP
SOYBEAN
SUGAR
VEGETABLE
WHEAT

SEE GLOSSARY SEE GLOSSARY

Connect the dots from I to 20.
Color the picture.

©School Zone Publishing Company 12501

SUIT UP!

Help Percy Penguin get to his suit.

End

MONKEY MAYHEM

Help Monty Monkey get to Simon Squirrel.

End

©School Zone Publishing Company 12501

NATIONAL PARKS

As people moved westward in the early 1800s, the United States became involved in protecting and preserving unique and special places. In 1872, the U.S. government established the first national park in the world, Yellowstone National Park. Since that time, more than 350 national parks have been created. Most national parks are preserved for their outstanding beauty, their unique wildlife, or the scientific importance of their natural features.

Old Faithful is a geyser in Yellowstone National Park. It erupts about every 91 minutes, shooting a stream of boiling water more than 100 feet high.

Think About It!

What are some of the problems facing national parks today?

```
N C                    E U A
  Y H       T S Y P W H J V B
C G I R U Y L P C N W S C N M K T
  N K J Y O E L A G R A N D C A N Y O N S C
  S C T M R W A L R D C E R A E N Y K E O H G U
F Y O S E M I T E B L H F K D S D L A F N E
I W N G I A L S V F G S O G L D W A E D R T W E G L
H X G O S D Y N I A L H B V W H E B O L Y M P I C Y M O H
L   N L O I E V E R G L A D E S A E T O B I H
  S C A N Y O N L A N D S A G T I K Y D E
  H A N C E S A C U K C H O R H O N L K X
  E   G   I V H F G L A U S N V Y N L
        E N E A M V E A C A V R E
        R Y N L E A G W L H J N
        V M A R N U S L O K
        A P C N V A T E Y G
        D Y U S D R O Y S
        E C V R O E O D
        S N H G X A N R
        T O A C H D H O
        B A D L A N D S
        G Y V O I S S V
        V L R W A N B A
        E N O M I
```

BADLANDS
CANYONLANDS
CARLSBAD CAVERNS
DEATH VALLEY
DENALI
EVERGLADES
GLACIER
GRAND CANYON
OLYMPIC
REDWOOD
SAGUARO
SHENANDOAH
YELLOWSTONE
YOSEMITE

Old Faithful

The smallest U.S. national park is Thaddeus Kosciuszko National Memorial in Pennsylvania. This monument honors a Polish patriot of the Revolutionary War and covers only 0.02 acres.

SEE GLOSSARY • SEE GLOSSARY

©School Zone Publishing Company 12501

GLORIOUS GIFTS

Help Rex Rhinoceros get to each of his three gifts.

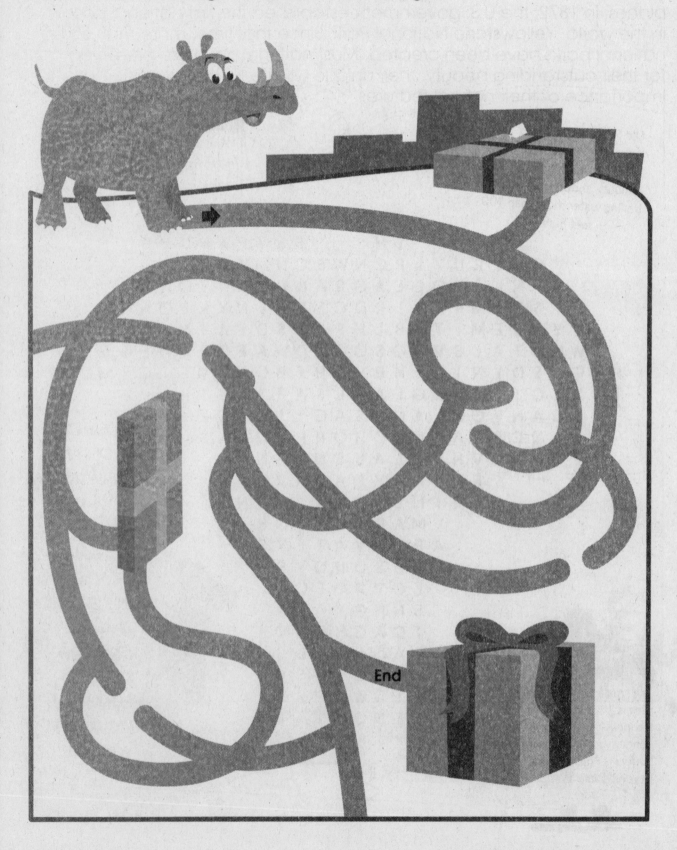

End

©School Zone Publishing Company 12501

AT THE BARBER SHOP

Find and circle the hidden pictures.

hot dog   mug   horn   glasses   battery   match   horseshoe   whistle

©School Zone Publishing Company 12501

Connect the dots from **1** to **20**.

Color the picture.

©School Zone Publishing Company 12501

FOLLOWING THE TREASURE MAP

Find and circle the hidden pictures.

accordion

cork

lug wrench

hot air balloon

coal cart

bottle

horse

clock

©School Zone Publishing Company 12501

MOUNTAINS

Mountains are found all over the world, even under the oceans. Movements of the earth's surface, volcanoes, and erosion can create mountains. A mountainous area of land usually lies 2,000 feet above its surroundings.

Mountain environments can vary greatly at different altitudes, which means that a variety of plants and animals can be found at different elevations. Most mountains are cold, snow-covered, and rocky near the peaks. Hiking, climbing, skiing, and snowboarding are a few of the sports enjoyed on mountains. Besides recreation, other uses for mountains include logging, mining, and grazing.

Think About It!

If you were going mountain climbing, what kind of clothing and equipment would you wear?

NOTABLE U.S. MOUNTAIN PEAKS

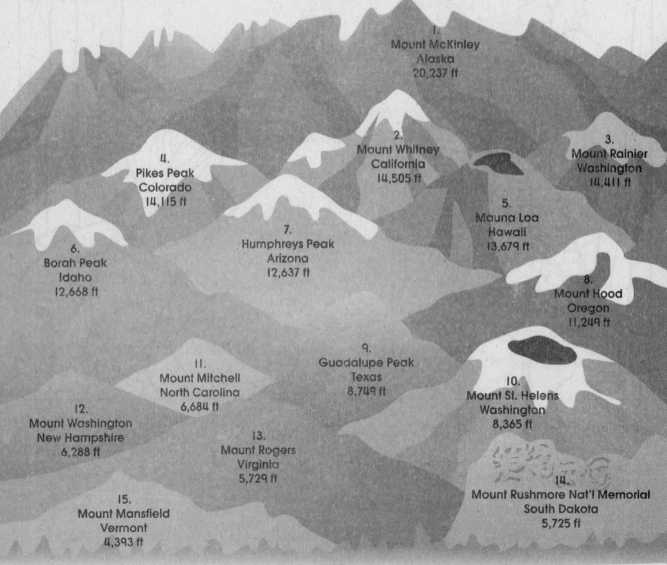

1. Mount McKinley
Alaska
20,237 ft

2. Mount Whitney
California
14,505 ft

3. Mount Rainier
Washington
14,411 ft

4. Pikes Peak
Colorado
14,115 ft

5. Mauna Loa
Hawaii
13,679 ft

6. Borah Peak
Idaho
12,668 ft

7. Humphreys Peak
Arizona
12,637 ft

8. Mount Hood
Oregon
11,249 ft

9. Guadalupe Peak
Texas
8,749 ft

10. Mount St. Helens
Washington
8,365 ft

11. Mount Mitchell
North Carolina
6,684 ft

12. Mount Washington
New Hampshire
6,288 ft

13. Mount Rogers
Virginia
5,729 ft

14. Mount Rushmore Nat'l Memorial
South Dakota
5,725 ft

15. Mount Mansfield
Vermont
4,393 ft

©School Zone Publishing Company 12501

ADIRONDACK
APPALACHIAN
BORAH
CASCADE
GREAT SMOKY
GUADALUPE
MAUNA LOA
PIKES PEAK
RAINIER
ROCKY
RUSHMORE
SIERRA NEVADA

SEE GLOSSARY · SEE GLOSSARY

```
        A   R A
        B V P D A N
        C T G R P T I U C
        T H D U N A S N P D
      R C P W S A K L I I I X
      R A E F H D D L A T E K E
    I A S D T M I E A P C H R E H
    A U R C H I O D T Y L F H L L S O
    B W N P A Y O R U A C I U W I W S P I
  H R O E I D N Y E O T L B D P S A X K E M
  S R I U R K E R I T N N V O R I E T N E Y A
  E T R X Y A D T I E I O D R E U A N L R K U K
  D V N C H S K R R W M A R H W L T O I N I
  S I E R R A N E V A D A C E U G A C B A N
  L O N D I G R E A T S M O K Y N O K H L N
  V A     I O K D P L H E G   P G Y N O I
        C H Y A             U C D A A
        G E                     R T T
```

The Rocky Mountains are part of the Continental Divide. They separate rivers that flow east to the Atlantic Ocean from rivers that flow west to the Pacific Ocean.

Yaks climb as high as 20,000 feet in the Himalayan Mountains. That's higher than any other animal.

Major U.S. Mountain Ranges

©School Zone Publishing Company 12501

PLAYFUL PUPPY

Find and circle the hidden pictures.

baseball bat · seal · bowling ball · apron · milk carton · moon · lamp · tennis racket

©School Zone Publishing Company 12501

HENHOUSE

Help Mother Hen and her chicks find their home.

©School Zone Publishing Company 12501

A SNAKE'S SNACK

Help Sandra Snake slither to the bunch of grapes.

End

©School Zone Publishing Company 12501

Connect the dots from **1** to **20**.
Color the picture.

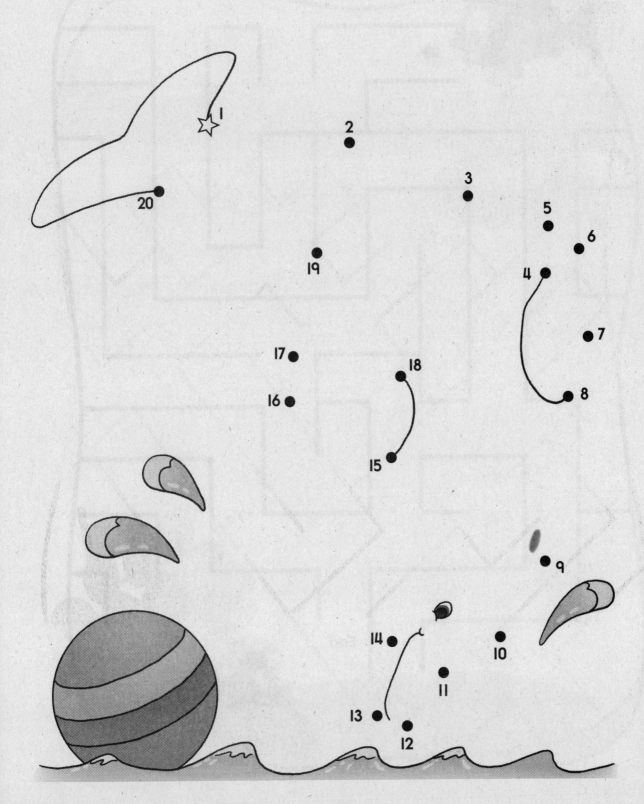

©School Zone Publishing Company 12501

FISH FAMILY

Help Father Fish swim to his children.

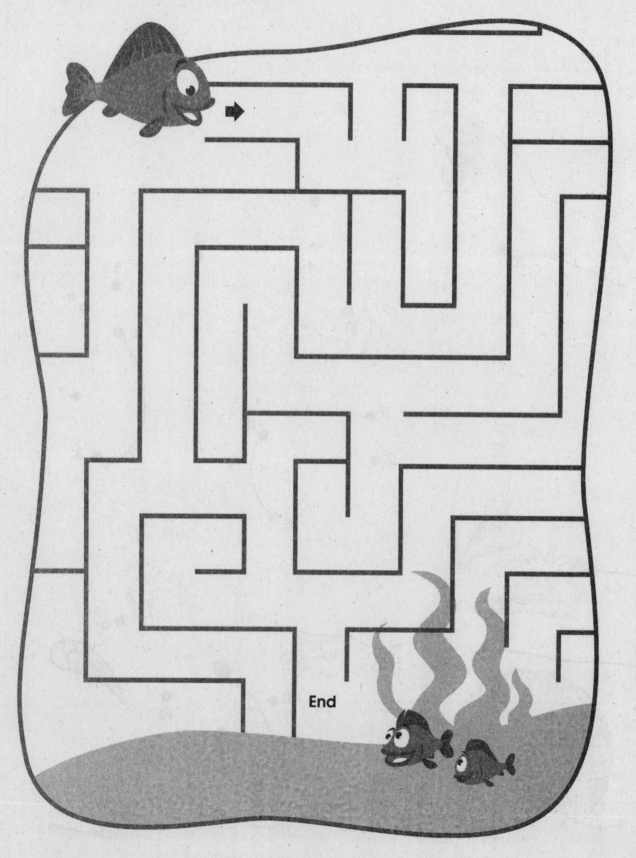

End

©School Zone Publishing Company 12501

FARMYARD WAKE-UP CALL

Find and circle the hidden pictures.

hand   alligator   rabbit   seeds   barrel   boomerang   spring   pogo stick

©School Zone Publishing Company 12501

Connect the dots from 1 to 20.
Color the picture.

©School Zone Publishing Company 12501

FLYING TO THE CASTLE

Help Drew Dragon fly to the castle.

End

©School Zone Publishing Company 12501

185

OCEANS AND SEAS

There are five oceans that surround the continents. Three of the great world oceans are the Pacific, the Atlantic, and the Indian. These three oceans meet around the continent of Antarctica in the Southern Hemisphere to form the Antarctic Ocean. The Arctic Ocean is on top of the earth.

The word sea can name any body of water, from a large lake to an ocean. Connected to each ocean are smaller bodies of water called seas, bays, and gulfs that are defined by land or islands.

The Mariana Trench in the Pacific Ocean is the deepest place known on earth. It has a maximum depth of almost 7 miles. Mt. Everest could fit inside of it.

Oceans cover over 70% of the earth and contain 97% of the world's water.

WORLD OCEANS

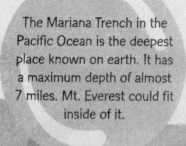

Arctic Ocean

Atlantic Ocean

Pacific Ocean

Pacific Ocean

Indian Ocean

Antarctic Ocean

The Dead Sea in the Middle East is so salty that animals cannot live in it. The Dead Sea contains 33.7% salt, which is 9.6 times saltier than the ocean.

186

©School Zone Publishing Company 12501

Flounder are saltwater fish that live on the bottom of bays and seas. Adult flounder have both eyes on one side of their heads.

Giant kelp, a large seaweed, is one of the fastest-growing plants in the world. It can grow almost two feet in one day.

```
        A T B E R N G
      L I B N O R T H Y T L A
      I L A R C T I C E K D R A C F O
    C E B R T N A T L A N T I C S I C H
    R H M E D I T E R R A N E A N F M P I N
    G Y G R R C I G A I I R W A D R I A T I C
    C A N I L H B E N E B T R I C Y H C N D B H
    E E N I T P A I B E B A L T I C I F I C O
    B G G H R N R H R D E T H N E F R T G
    K D A O T C I E I E Y A U D I I K N
    L W T F B D Y N L A T N I L C I K
    R M A N T A R C T I C B A P M T
      E B F C N T R I S G N N F A
      D     H C O C O C H I E O
          P I F O P A C F P
          A N R K N I A
          L B L A C K R
          C Y A T L S
          I C L F A
```

SEAS

ADRIATIC
AEGEAN   CHINA
BALTIC   CORAL
BARENTS   MEDITERRANEAN
BERING   NORTH
BLACK   RED
CARIB-   TASMAN
BEAN

SEE GLOSSARY · SEE GLOSSARY

OCEANS

ANTARCTIC
ARCTIC
ATLANTIC
INDIAN
PACIFIC

ON THE FRONT PORCH

Find and circle the hidden pictures.

bread   lettuce   saw   teapot   button   eggplant   bow tie   newspaper

188

©School Zone Publishing Company 12501

Find and circle the hidden pictures.

pretzel   toothbrush   bee   sock   bottle   mug   cloud   microphone

©School Zone Publishing Company 12501

LAUGHING LIONS

Help Larry Lion get to his cub.

End

©School Zone Publishing Company 12501

Connect the dots from **1** to **20**.
Color the picture.

©School Zone Publishing Company 12501

ARCTIC AMIGOS

Help Sabrina Seagull fly to Wally Walrus.

End

©School Zone Publishing Company 12501

Connect the dots from **1** to **20**.
Color the picture.

©School Zone Publishing Company 12501

DESERTS

Deserts are regions that receive minimal rainfall. Deserts are also identified by the types of soil and vegetation that exist in an area. Most deserts are in warm climates, but the North Pole and South Pole can be considered deserts as well.

Deserts located in warm climates are very hot. Some of the animals that live there have adapted to the hot, dry conditions. They keep cool in the shade and can go for long periods of time without water. Their bodies are good at moving quickly over sand or burrowing into it.

Think About It!

How do people protect themselves in hot climates?

WORLD DESERTS

Great Basin

Mojave

Painted
Sonoran

Chihuahuan

Sechura

Atacama

Patagonian

Karakum

Taklamakan

Gobi

Sahara

Thar

Arabian

Namib

Kalahari

Australian Desert

Deserts usually have very high daytime temperatures and very low nighttime temperatures due to low humidity.

An oasis is a place in the desert with enough water to support wells and springs.

©School Zone Publishing Company 12501

The saguaro cactus can grow as tall as 50 feet. They grow in the southwestern United States and northwestern Mexico.

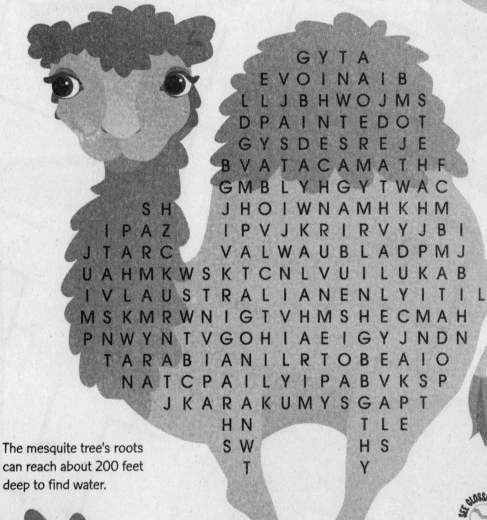

```
        G Y T A
        E V O I N A I B
        L L J B H W O J M S
        D P A I N T E D O T
        G Y S D E S R E J E
        B V A T A C A M A T H F
        G M B L Y H G Y T W A C
    S H   J H O I W N A M H K H M
  I P A Z   I P V J K R I R V Y J B I
J T A R C   V A L W A U B L A D P M J
U A H M K W S K T C N L V U I L U K A B
I V L A U S T R A L I A N E N L Y I T I L
M S K M R W N I G T V H M S H E C M A H
P N W Y N T V G O H I A E I G Y J N D N
  T A R A B I A N I L R T O B E A I O
  N A T C P A I L Y I P A B V K S P
    J K A R A K U M Y S G A P T
    H N             T L E
    S W             H S
    T               H Y
```

The mesquite tree's roots can reach about 200 feet deep to find water.

SEE GLOSSARY • SEE GLOSSARY

Camels are made for the desert. They can withstand heat, travel long distances, and survive for days without water. Their humps are made of fat that can be used for energy. They can even clamp their nostrils and lips shut to keep out blowing sand.

ARABIAN

ATACAMA

AUSTRALIAN

DEATH VALLEY

GOBI

KALAHARI

KARAKUM

MOJAVE

NAMIB

PAINTED

PATAGONIAN

SAHARA

THAR

©School Zone Publishing Company 12501

SILLY SEAL

Help Sal Seal get to the bucket of water.

End

©School Zone Publishing Company 12501

CITY STREETS

Find and circle the hidden pictures.

comb   battery   pencil   gift   doughnut   glass   ring   envelope

197

©School Zone Publishing Company 12501

BRIGHT BUDDIES

Find and circle the hidden pictures.

book   thimble   bottle   marker   measuring cup   shovel   Saturn   stool

©School Zone Publishing Company 12501

Connect the dots from **1** to **20**.
Color the picture.

©School Zone Publishing Company 12501

Connect the dots from **1** to **20**.
Color the picture.

©School Zone Publishing Company 12501

PREHISTORIC PALS

Help Patty Pterodactyl get to her dinosaur friend.

End

©School Zone Publishing Company 12501

RIVERS

Rivers have always been important to people. Many major cities developed near rivers because rivers provided the chief form of transportation for trade, travel, and exploration. For centuries, farmers have found river valleys and plains to be especially fertile farmland.

Today, rivers also provide electric power for homes and industries. Dammed rivers store water for irrigation and turn turbines for electric generators. Think of all the ordinary activities that use water: drinking, cooking, bathing, flushing toilets, washing clothes and dishes, and watering lawns are a few. Much of this water comes from rivers.

World River Lengths (Miles)

River	Length
Nile (Africa)	4,160
Amazon (South America)	4,000
Yangtze (Asia)	3,917
Congo (Africa)	2,922
Lena (Asia)	2,734
Mississippi (North America)	2,350
Missouri (North America)	2,341
Volga (Eastern Europe)	2,266
Yukon (North America)	1,979
Rio Grande (North America)	1,900
Danube (Europe)	1,776

©School Zone Publishing Company 12501

```
L H N S W Z I W O T I
C E Z V A L L E Y Y O
I N N P F U T N K P A
V K S S I R L A M I S S I S S I S S I P P I C O L I
H O E M K O R M U L A M F Y P M Y K C T U N M
A D L N I N N I D T V S N N M I S S O U R I G
O A Y G T R I O G R A N D E N A Z O N I O L R
Y N N U A I U P T A E M P I H W Y R G D N E E
G U V K L V I T W A T U A P Z T G H O N Y C N
H B K N K E T R S R G I H Z T L I V B G H G C
C E C O L R D Z I R E V O Y O Y A N G T Z E S
T Y F B N B C H D T N Y I N A N H T U R I N T
```

AMAZON	LENA	RIO GRANDE	YANGTZE
CONGO	MISSISSIPPI	RIVER	YUKON
DANUBE	MISSOURI	VALLEY	
IRRIGATION	NILE	VOLGA	

SEE GLOSSARY · SEE GLOSSARY

The Nile River is the world's longest river, but the Amazon River carries 200 times more water.

©School Zone Publishing Company 12501

Connect the dots from 1 to 25.
Color the picture.

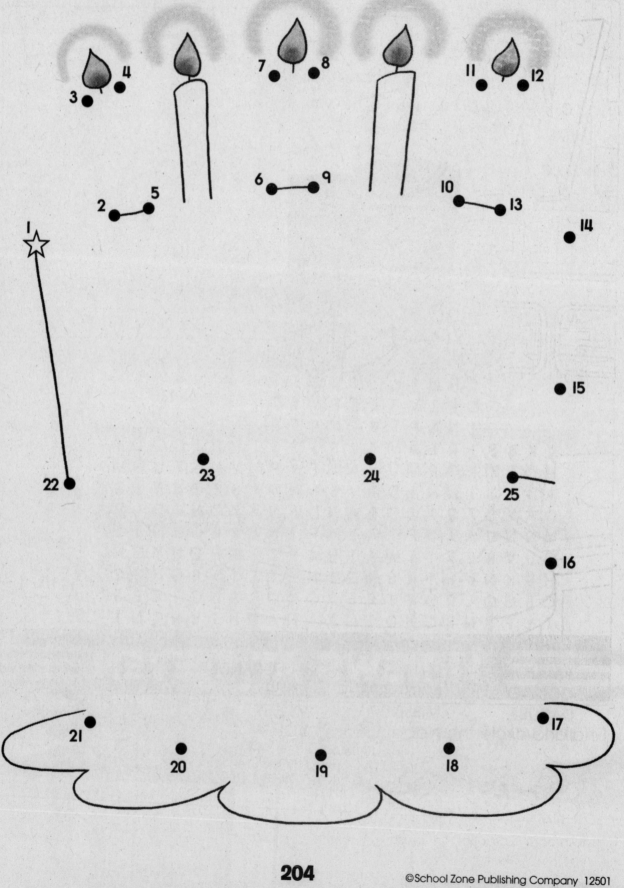

©School Zone Publishing Company 12501

TODAY'S TOP STORY

Find and circle the hidden pictures.

mushroom   cracker   brush   shorts   peach   piano   pencil   flower

©School Zone Publishing Company 12501

SNOW DAY

Help Ray Reindeer get to the snowman.

End

©School Zone Publishing Company 12501

Connect the dots from **1** to **25**.
Color the picture.

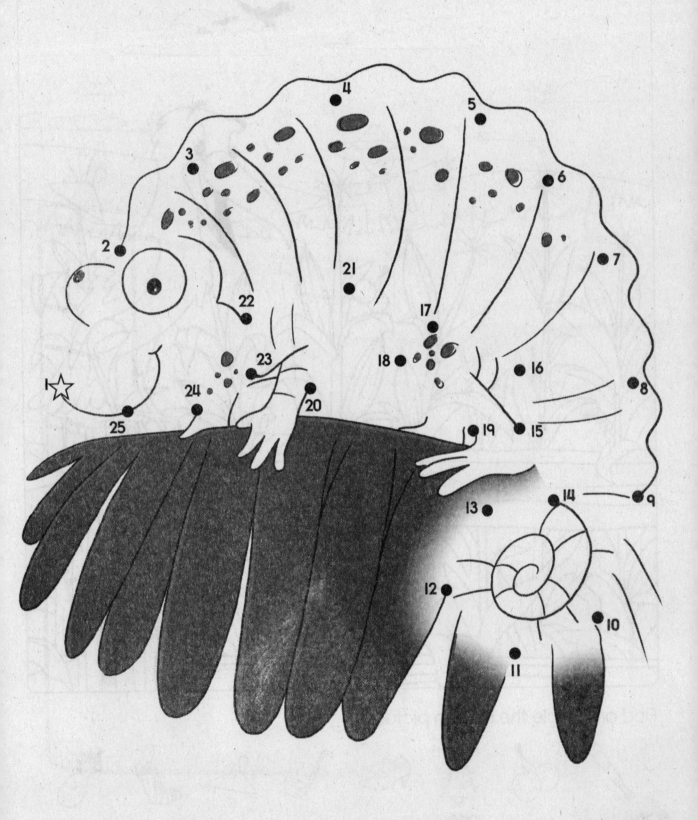

©School Zone Publishing Company 12501

I'M NOT SCARED!

Find and circle the hidden pictures.

| telescope | cherries | pine tree | shoe | ladle | hanger | caterpillar | pineapple |

208

©School Zone Publishing Company 12501

A BOY'S BIRD

Help Bailey Bird fly to the boy.

End

©School Zone Publishing Company 12501

NATURAL DISASTERS

Natural disasters are sudden and extremely unfortunate events that affect many people. Meteorologists study weather and the earth to try to predict and understand natural disasters.

Different parts of the world are at risk for different types of natural disasters. In mountainous areas, avalanches are huge drifts of snow that rush downward. Volcanoes erupt hot gases and melted rock from miles below the earth's surface. Tornadoes, hurricanes, and typhoons are caused by tremendous winds. Earthquakes result from moving plates deep in the earth. Tsunamis are huge ocean waves caused by undersea earthquakes or volcanoes.

Think About It!

What kinds of natural disasters might occur where you live? What safety precautions can you take during a natural disaster?

Use a word from the word search to label each type of natural disaster.

Other names for hurricanes include "typhoons" and "tropical cyclones."

©School Zone Publishing Company 12501

Word List:
- AVALANCHE
- BLIZZARD
- EARTHQUAKE
- FLOOD
- HURRICANE
- METEOROLOGIST
- ROCKSLIDE
- TORNADO
- TSUNAMI
- TYPHOON
- VOLCANO

SEE GLOSSARY

Word Search Grid:

```
E A L O   N O K  Y U   U A Q   M A
B Y R O H U R R I C A N E T Y A I S U N A I N
C L C Y O N D C S V T Z V A B L I Z Z A R D M T R C
T F E D O I G I L N W R L C D V S M K X F R C Y H Y
S D O A Y O S T M E T E O R O L O G I S T R N P K E
U N R F R A G C W N Y F R C Z I D L H U N F T H F C
G G T I A T D T P G P U Q V K M T G C O I N G O A G
B L O A R S H O Y H N H I C H S Y F I A U H Y O H N
I I R U I U I Q R O N U V Z I F L O O D N X F N I
L Z N B C N C R U R O L O G Z E T I R S T O L E K
K Z A K Q A V A L A N C H E K A K C D O R G O I T
L Y D L N M W N L O K H N A Q L R Y L E M K D L
Q M O U E I U R R W C E M L K U O N T
N U N T S N     S T   B L I
U O E O K
S   N I
```

Experts sometimes cause avalanches on purpose. They use explosives to send snow down a mountain. This prevents the snow from building up and causing a more dangerous avalanche.

©School Zone Publishing Company 12501

Connect the dots from **1** to **25**.
Color the picture.

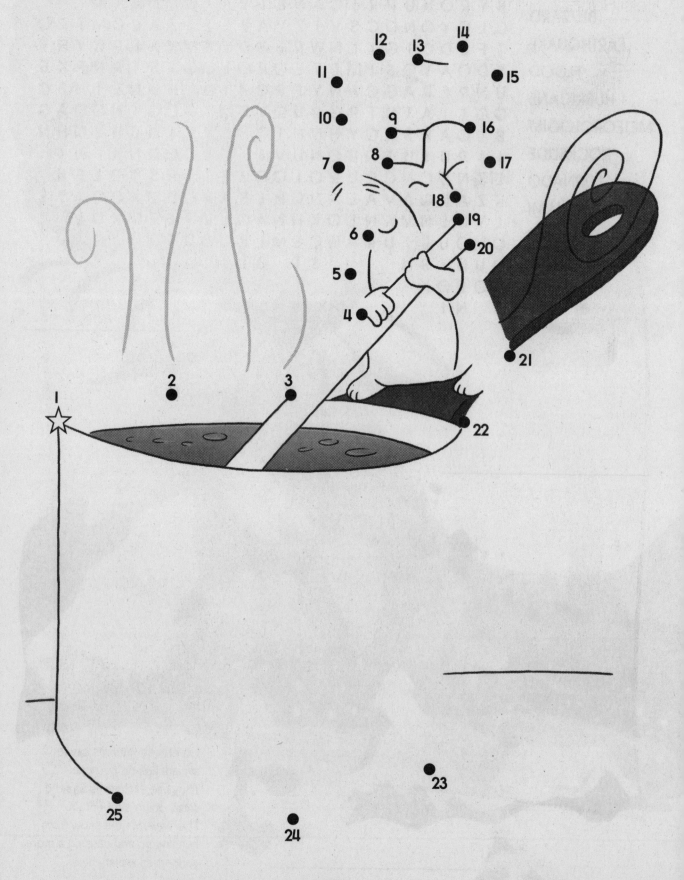

©School Zone Publishing Company 12501

FOREST FRIENDS

Help Hannah Hummingbird fly to Marco Moose.

©School Zone Publishing Company 12501

Connect the dots from **1** to **25**.
Color the picture.

©School Zone Publishing Company 12501

DIVING DUO

Help Olivia Octopus get to the scuba diving salamander.

End

©School Zone Publishing Company 12501

UNIVERSE

The universe includes everything that exists anywhere in space and time. It consists of all matter, light, and other forms of energy. The universe includes Earth, everything on Earth and within it, all of the planets, and everything in the solar system.

Scientists do not know the size of the universe. Astronomers think that the universe is very large, perhaps infinite in volume. Astronomers cannot be sure because the universe is constantly evolving. There are different theories about the universe. One theory says that it is expanding. No one knows which theory, if any, is correct.

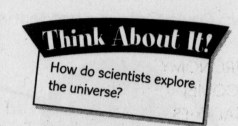

Think About It!

How do scientists explore the universe?

The Moon's near side always faces Earth and has been studied in detail. The Moon's far side always faces away from Earth. It was first photographed in 1959 by a Russian space probe.

THE MILKY WAY GALAXY

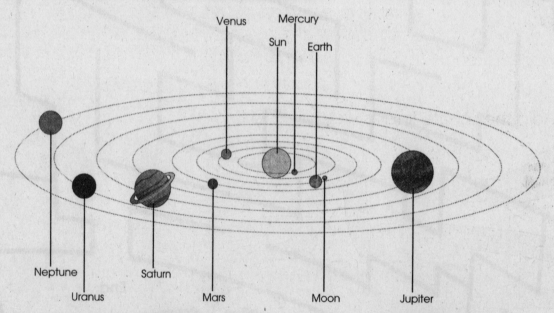

Venus
Mercury
Sun
Earth
Neptune
Uranus
Saturn
Mars
Moon
Jupiter

The Hoba West Meteorite is the largest known meteorite. It is estimated to weigh over 60 tons. The meteorite landed in Africa and is too massive to move.

The planet Saturn is known for its bright rings, which are mostly made of ice.

©School Zone Publishing Company 12501

ASTRONOMY
COMET
GALAXIES
JUPITER
MARS
MERCURY
MOON
PLANETS
SATURN
STARS
SUN
UNIVERSE
URANUS
VENUS

```
              J W X Y
          T E R B P V W A V T H
        M E V C W R E M U S Y N T C
      A R U S U N F U S A T U I D E S
      S R E S Q X S J E W Y R E R A V R V
      D A T W G T D M F T P V O S F A L X E F
      J X R Y N A E R E S U G N X A L N G R Y
    N Y A E H V G L N T J N C O M E T O U I T E
    M T P T L Y P X A N Y F I M X X F R N S U I
    P S L H N A O J U X R X T Y J N T K I S J T
    N O A S R E V O T K I N Y R A U E R V C K R
    M L N V X S J U P I T E R T C G P L E S X L
    T N E M E R S E L T S M S E V U H M R T A M
      Y T J E N H T U D N V O N E X A L S V U
      D S C S M U M E R C U R Y O M L N E I S
      R T Z B S S R T N X D V B O N C Y L
        Q A I T S T N V U D I O O X R T
          N R G E I J S A T U R N U M
          S S V U X L G S Y H C
              N T Q R S V
```

Help the shuttle find its way back to Earth.

©School Zone Publishing Company 12501

Connect the dots from **1** to **25**.

Color the picture.

218

©School Zone Publishing Company 12501

OUT AT SEA

Help Wilma Whale swim to Margo Mouse.

End

©School Zone Publishing Company 12501

PIGEON PALS

Help Pablo Pigeon fly to his feathered friends.

End

©School Zone Publishing Company 12501

Connect the dots from 1 to 25.
Color the picture.

©School Zone Publishing Company 12501

ENVIRONMENTS

Animals live all over the world, from frozen tundras to hot deserts. An animal's natural environment is called its habitat. Many animals migrate from one habitat to another. Other animals have adapted to their environment by developing special characteristics. For instance, heavy fur protects some animals from the cold.

Think About It!

How do you think early humans adapted to different environments?

In what type of habitat do you live? How have you adapted?

Often, animals in similar habitats in different parts of the world have similar characteristics. For example, kangaroo rats in North America look like gerbils that live in the Sahara Desert.

```
      L T A     R M A
    A B R S H A D I U S A   S
    C N A R A I N F O R E S T C
  D D W M O H F N E D O K T C W H D
  N S E O E E W S C V G R E U A E O
  G Y T U O D T F A B R F E F M P U F
  C G W L N G D R C T D N D S S J M G E
  D E P F T R A L I H C S D E V T H S N L
  C I F I A C O R A L R E E F W R E C B A P
  N U O S I S J O R N B H S R U Y I R W M Y J
    V D G N W U K S Y D X E E N T M U K A O P
  P O L A R I C E S M P L R B I A P B E L M I
  T F M M X A G H L D W H T L C M Y L C Y M P
  G B A S N C S T N S F T Y N O S W A M P C N
    L N M A R S H L A N D O R F B N I T D I
      H L C U L I P L R P D N N D P R A
        G A T A         W
        T U N D R A R
        A G S D O U
        I H R T
        N C S A
        K A T W
        H W S
```

CORAL REEF

DESERT

FOREST

GRASSLAND

MARSHLAND

MOUNTAIN

POLAR ICE

RAINFOREST

SCRUBLAND

 SWAMP

TUNDRA

WOODLAND

Some plants and animals live outside their natural environments in zoos, aquariums, and botanical gardens.

©School Zone Publishing Company 12303

WINDOW SHOPPING

Find and circle the hidden pictures.

briefcase   binoculars   flute   laptop   radish   tooth   pig   iron

©School Zone Publishing Company 12501

FOREST FRIENDS

Find and circle the hidden pictures.

moon   straw   lipstick   canoe   acorn   bowl   guitar   heart

©School Zone Publishing Company 12501

NIGHTTIME VISIT

Help Ollie Owl visit Gary Groundhog.

End

©School Zone Publishing Company 12501

HATCHING TIME

Help Tiffany Turkey find her egg.

End

©School Zone Publishing Company 12501

GARDEN FLOWERS

A flower is the blossom of a plant. Most plants have flowers. Although we admire blossoms for their beauty, the function of blossoms is to make seeds.

Garden flowers are simply cultivated wild flowers. Some kinds of garden flowers are exactly like the wild ones. Others have been bred so that their blooms are more attractive than those of the wild variety. Garden flowers can be divided into three main groups based on how long they live: annuals live a year or less, biennials live two years, and perennials live for several years.

```
        E B F I M
        B V I O L E T
      A I C K B K A P
      T M S R D S M H
      Y A S A N I E S A S
    H Z I N N I A R L W R N
    H P B R P O P P Y P F I S
  S Q E P H F E I D E H C G E
  A U O D A O D K R D I A O V
  N D N C D X D Y A D N H L Z
  C A Y F L G A F G A I O D J
  L O V O L L B F O E U L O L
  E J S J B O M J N S M L X J P A
  C D E M N V W E U U G Y R H A S
  G O R C O E C E N C C H C S N T
  V T R X G S I V R T G O W G S E
    A R P E T U N I A C S P Y R
    G C B A N E C D K C M X U
```

Annuals
COSMOS
MARIGOLD
PANSY
PETUNIA
SNAPDRAGON
SUNFLOWER
ZINNIA

Biennials
FOXGLOVE
HOLLYHOCK

Perennials
ASTER
DELPHINIUM
PEONY
POPPY
VIOLET

Many insects rely on flowers to provide the food they need to survive.

SEE GLOSSARY • SEE GLOSSARY

227

©School Zone Publishing Company 12501

SUMMER SEASON FUN

A season is one of the four periods of the year: spring, summer, autumn, and winter. The seasons change because the tilt of the earth's axis provides different amounts of sunlight to different places on the earth. Each season lasts about three months and brings changes in temperature, weather, and sunlight.

Summer is the warmest season of the year. The Northern Hemisphere, the northern half of the earth, has summer weather during late June, July, August, and early September. During these months, warm weather encourages many of the activities that we identify with summer.

Think About It!

Think of things you can do with a group of friends during the summer season. Try to put on a play, go stargazing, or plant a garden.

SEE GLOSSARY · SEE GLOSSARY

BARBECUES
BASEBALL
BIKING
BOCCIE
CAMPING
CARNIVALS
CROQUET
FIREWORKS
FISHING
GOLF
HIKING
PICNICS
SOCCER
SWIMMING
TENNIS
VOLLEYBALL

```
        C R M O I N G
      O V M F Q A B L F T U W
M B A S E B A L L I S R S V S N P Q
Y A U O M I R L G S R N R O L R I S
W R J R H K O H G H O I A L S K C A
S B O C C I E A B I E V C L E Z N B
R E W Z D N C T E N D A B E K O I Z
H C C H C G D F M G O L F Y D T C
E U E A I K O Z B N A S E B C H S
D E O C R O Q U E T M D W A V P O
H S J B M G J M O K N O Q L J J
A U D E N C U S E U A M E L H I
O S C F I R E W O R K S Q T B V
X O G R G L K I C G T Y N X O
T C S A X C A M P I N G B J S
E C B V R N B M N K S R K Z
N E C A H I K I N G C Y I
N R F O B C C N C D
I W B L C A L G
S D S U O I X
  T E B J I S
```

©School Zone Publishing Company 12501

Connect the dots from **1** to **25**.

Color the picture.

PADDLING DOWN THE RIVER

Find and circle the hidden pictures.

rolling pin   duck   ship   pie   pan   yield sign   hat   boot

©School Zone Publishing Company 12501

HOBBIES

A hobby can be almost any kind of leisure activity that people do during their spare time. Most hobbies fall into one of four general categories, which include the arts (painting, dance, music), collecting (sports cards, autographs, dolls, shells), handicrafts (cooking, photography, sewing, woodworking), and games and sports (skiing, tennis, chess, fishing).

In the past, hobbies were largely limited to the wealthy. The average person was too busy earning a living to find time to pursue a hobby. Today, people of almost any age and income level can enjoy hobbies for pleasure or relaxation.

Think About It!

What are a few of your favorite hobbies?

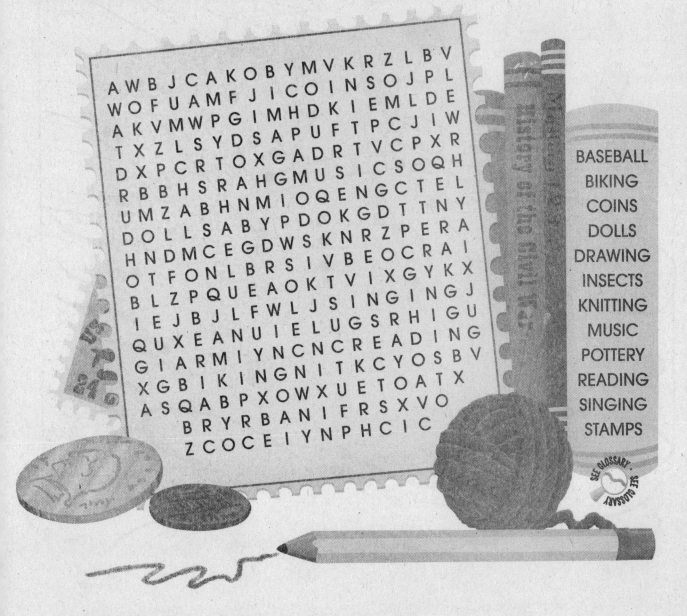

BASEBALL
BIKING
COINS
DOLLS
DRAWING
INSECTS
KNITTING
MUSIC
POTTERY
READING
SINGING
STAMPS

Connect the dots from **1** to **25**.
Color the picture.

©School Zone Publishing Company 12501

HORSES IN THE STABLE

Find and circle the hidden pictures.

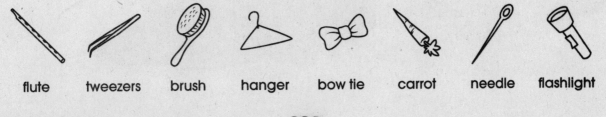

flute   tweezers   brush   hanger   bow tie   carrot   needle   flashlight

©School Zone Publishing Company 12501

DANCE

Dance is among the oldest human art forms. Dance can express emotions or tell a story. Music usually accompanies dance, setting the rhythm, tempo, and mood for movement.

Some kinds of dances we watch, and some dances we participate in for pleasure. People dance for different reasons. For thousands of years, people danced for ceremonial, celebratory, and religious reasons. Dance also strengthens social connections, especially during courtship. Many people dance just for the fun of it. When a dance is performed before an audience, it becomes a form of drama.

Think About It!

What are some dances that you would like to try? Try inventing a new style that's all your own.

SEE GLOSSARY · SEE GLOSSARY

```
        R D I S C O H
      F O X T R O T A I W A
    A D B Y F S K I S B P S T O A
  S B S R S A M B A D F H V R J S
  H A A H R O B O L E R O N U O W H
  F L L A H N H I W K C P E M E I R
K A L S D A X E O       A D B D N Y
X N E A C A O X         T A N G O
A T T A M L A N         O H A
O L F M I E E A
  E J B N J N O J
  U D E U N U C E U
  G C R E Z E C O N
  S C O T I L L I O N
    A N I M Z H S R
    R K W A L T Z
        P C
```

BALLET
BOLERO
COTILLION
DISCO
FLAMENCO
FOX-TROT
HIP-HOP
MINUET
RUMBA

SALSA
SAMBA
SWING
TANGO
WALTZ

©School Zone Publishing Company 12501

Connect the dots from **1** to **25**.
Color the picture.

©School Zone Publishing Company 12501

DRIBBLING UP THE COURT

Find and circle the hidden pictures.

doghouse   tongs   suit   mug   cactus   abacus   soap   seven

236

©School Zone Publishing Company 12501

Connect the dots from **1** to **25**.

Color the picture.

©School Zone Publishing Company 12501

GOING UNDERCOVER

Find and circle the hidden pictures.

 scale

 paddle ball

purse

flipper

jelly bean

noodle

snowflake

 ice-cream cone

238

©School Zone Publishing Company 12501

BOATS

Boats have been used for thousands of years. Early boats were used for work and travel. Through the years, pleasure boats developed from these workboats.

Boats are usually smaller than ships and are generally used in inland lakes or protected coastal areas. Many boats use motors or sails for power. Other boats rely on paddle wheels, water jets, air fans, or human power.

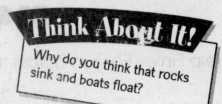

Think About It!

Why do you think that rocks sink and boats float?

CANOE
CATAMARAN
FERRY
GONDOLA
HOUSEBOAT
HYDROFOIL
JUNK
KAYAK

PONTOON
ROWBOAT
SAMPAN
SLOOP
STEAMBOAT
TUGBOAT
YACHT

SEE GLOSSARY · SEE GLOSSARY

```
                                            D
                                    I     R C
                              A G           M G S
                        S T          S A N R D A
                        R R Z        R G R O P J X
                  P S I E            O C G S W B I A T
                  E O L C            N E A E B F C E U Y
                  P K N O A          Z X J T O K A D G E
                  D W A T O          D Z O Y A C H T B I
                  L A U A Y O P       I G N D I T M C N O H
                  V B E O Z A O       F E R R Y D O A O A O
                  B J C J U N K N     J C H L C P Z S J R T J
                  D E X N U V E U     A N U U W U L A E R A I
                  S T C A N O E C T   G O N D O L A C M C P L N
                  H Y D R O F O I L   G J P O X A J P T P V B F
                  A D E P M I         A H O U S E B O A T A S T
                                      S T E A M B O A T S N I
                                      V G O X R B K D C J
```

The Dover Museum in Britain has a wooden boat on display that is thought to be about 3,000 years old.

©School Zone Publishing Company 12501

FAST-MOVING FOX

Help Finley Fox run across the bridges.

End

©School Zone Publishing Company 12501

DOGS

Dogs have lived as pets for thousands of years. All breeds of domestic dogs, from the Great Dane to the Chihuahua, are descended from the wolf. Today, the American Kennel Club recognizes over 150 dog breeds, and there are even more throughout the world. With so many different breeds, dogs are more varied in their appearance and behavior than any other domestic animal.

Wolf: dog's ancestor

Dachshund: curious & mischievous

Chihuahua: intelligent & alert

Collie: kind & loyal

Saint Bernard: gentle & obedient

The greyhound is the fastest breed of dog. They can reach speeds of up to 45 miles per hour.

AIREDALE
BEAGLE
BOXER
BULLDOG
CHIHUAHUA
COLLIE
DACHSHUND
GERMAN SHEPHERD
GREYHOUND
LABRADOR RETRIEVER
POINTER
POODLE
SAINT BERNARD
SCHNAUZER
YORKSHIRE TERRIER

```
        Y R A C M L A K Z C W
      S P O O D L E A S P E S O F H
      C C L R A A Y F B R E O T C L I
    D W H M K F B H B R E Y H I W N L K
    S E I W S B U U O E R L U A N O L I
  G Y T H V H S L A X D A C H S H T N D E
  E B L U G I K L H E O N I S Y J Q E E H
  I O L A B R A D O R R E T R I E V E R D
  U Z I H E E N O A R R E F W E A O U A F
  T G U A T A G R E Y H O U N D D L M L
  R Q A G E U A Y F T E D N A M A L B
  A R L R Z S C H N A U Z E R E L L
  M X E R E D D W I X L E R Y L O E
  W S A I N T B E R N A R D W A G P
      G E R M A N S H E P H E R D
      R O D A C H S H U N D P
        P K R N P V E
```

©School Zone Publishing Company 12501

JUST HOPPED BY

Help Kacy Koala get to Keegan Kangaroo.

End

©School Zone Publishing Company 12501

Connect the dots from **1** to **25**.
Color the picture.

©School Zone Publishing Company 12501

Connect the dots from **1** to **25**.

Color the picture.

244

©School Zone Publishing Company 12501

HOW ANIMALS PROTECT THEMSELVES

To avoid danger from enemies, animals have developed different ways to protect themselves. The best protection against a predator is to avoid being seen. To do this, some animals leave their homes mainly or only at night. Many animals camouflage themselves by blending in with their surroundings. Animals, such as the chameleon, even change color to blend with the background. Flight, either by running or flying, is another way to avoid danger. Some animals play dead. Other animals fight with sharp hooves, claws, or quills. Skunks use a foul-smelling odor, and some snakes use a poisonous venom.

```
Y F L I G H T J
Y A S M N P S X B H A C
R S R V P C L A W S I R F D
C H O R N S R A B I N D M N H
D A H N E I E Y F V E I O M R
K X S M E L L S I I A U N R V
K I Q D O D F A N G S X G D
S M M A U W A G H V D V
D P I O F F D D T E C
E E M J L L E I N
E E I U A A N O
C D D C D D G M
I O X R B E E
P Y M P Y C
```

ARMOR	FLIGHT	SMELLS
CAMOUFLAGE	HIDING	SPEED
CLAWS	HORNS	VENOM
FANGS	MIMICRY	
FIGHTING	PLAYING DEAD	

Think About It!

Look at an animal that lives near your house. How does the animal protect itself?

©School Zone Publishing Company 12501

THAT HOUSE LOOKS HAUNTED!

OLDWOOD MANOR

Find and circle the hidden pictures.

wrench

bell

battery

cucumber

top hat

moon

purse

ghost

©School Zone Publishing Company 12501

Find and circle the hidden pictures.

baseball cap   baseball   spoon   seeds   spider   cat   radish   rolling pin

©School Zone Publishing Company 12501

BEST BUDDIES

Help Parker Pony gallop to the cowboy.

End

©School Zone Publishing Company 12501

CAVES

Caves are naturally occurring underground chambers formed out of rocks. There are many different types of caves - some with hidden lakes and waterfalls formed by water trickling down through rocks, such as limestone. Some caves are no bigger than a closet, but others are huge.

Deep inside a cave, there is no light and no day or night. The temperature hardly changes with the seasons. Plants cannot grow deep within a cave because there is no light. Some animals enter caves for shelter or to hunt for prey. Other animals spend their entire lives in this environment.

BATS
BEARS
BEETLES
BOBCATS
CENTIPEDES
COCKROACHES
CRICKETS
FISH
FOXES
OWLS
RACCOONS
RATS
SALAMANDERS
SNAILS
SPIDERS
SWALLOWS
WORMS

SEE GLOSSARY · SEE GLOSSARY

Think About It!

Think of some ways that animals have adapted to the cold, dark environment of caves.

```
        A F I R
        O W L S R D A I
        B P X O A I B O C
        S A S D A T M E A O A
      K C S N A I L S A E S C S
    B J E K R L S R R G T R K R
    Z O R N F H A R O H G L O R I
    P B A T S D M H N E I E W O C
    L C C I S W A L L O W S D A
    U A C P N D N A D G P I L C
    A T O E X A D L T B F I S H
    S O D E B E A R S Y I O E
    N E R B R J X F O X E S
    S S Q E S P I D E R S G
    Y A R W O V P C N X C
      C R I C K E T S Y G
      R O V K I P C E S
      A W O R M S
```

Geology is a science that deals with the history of the earth and its life as recorded in rocks.

©School Zone Publishing Company 12501

TURTLE TIME

Find and circle the hidden pictures.

ladybug   moon   picnic basket   chess piece   squirrel   cucumber   dollar   thermometer

©School Zone Publishing Company 12501

Connect the dots from 1 to 25.
Color the picture.

©School Zone Publishing Company 12501

DON'T BUG ME!

Help the praying mantis get to the ladybug.

©School Zone Publishing Company 12501

Connect the dots from 1 to 25.
Color the picture.

©School Zone Publishing Company 12501

HIBERNATION AND DORMANCY

During the winter months, as temperatures drop and food becomes scarce, some animals hibernate or go into a state of dormancy in order to survive the harsh conditions. Hibernation is a resting state during which the animal's body temperature falls, breathing decreases, and body processes slow. One type of animal that hibernates is the chipmunk. Some other animals, such as bears, go into a resting state called dormancy during the winter. Dormancy differs from hibernation in that the animal's body temperature does not drop significantly and the animal can awaken quickly if danger threatens.

Think About It!

Have you ever wondered what it would be like to sleep all winter long?

BATS
BEARS
CHIPMUNKS
FROGS
LADYBUGS

LEMURS
LIZARDS
MARMOTS
MICE
NIGHTHAWKS

SNAKES
SQUIRRELS
SWIFTS
TURTLES

SEE GLOSSARY · SEE GLOSSARY

```
        D A J C I C O
        W A B A T S M N D B
      I S N L P Y A S A E S P M
      B P W I R S R B E A R S R L
    H R H I Z G R M H G R O Q I A H
    E U M E A E H N E I E D U C D S
    I L E M U R S L T C J D F I A Y W A
    U N H N S D T P I H X O N R F B I S
    S N A K E S U L A I A L X R O U F K
    O A B L M K R V E P C W B E W G T L
    U M A R M O T S J M O T K L J S S P
    S Y N I E L N L U E U A S E R H R
      C P C R E V M N C N C G
        G E R S U V K P Y T
        P A O T W S N
          X J E R
```

©School Zone Publishing Company 12501

HAPPY HIPPO

Help Riley Rabbit visit Haley Hippo.

End

©School Zone Publishing Company 12501

NAP TIME

Find and circle the hidden pictures.

flag   soup can   lemon   ice pop   button   rocking chair   snail   balloon

©School Zone Publishing Company 12501

MAGNIFICENT MUD BATH

Help Penny Pig join her friend in the mud puddle.

End

©School Zone Publishing Company 12501

Connect the dots from 1 to 25.
Color the picture.

©School Zone Publishing Company 12501

HEADGEAR

People wear hats and headgear for several reasons. Hats may be worn for protection from the climate or from injury. People also wear hats that identify their occupation. Still other hats are worn for decoration or as an accessory. Hats vary widely in material and style, depending largely on climate, people's customs, and the reason for wearing the hat.

Think About It!

What would make the perfect hat? Think of the size, shape, materials, and decorations you would use.

BERET
BONNET
BOWLER HAT
CAP
CLOCHE
COWBOY HAT
CROWN
FEZ
HELMET
HOOD
SOMBRERO
TOP HAT
TURBAN

```
              T R C H V P
          T A M X C I C W B N A I
        D C P W A C A P Z G Y T K O V
      R S N Z Y A S A Z B H Q I H R S I
      X R O R S R B O W L E R H A T B R
    H T K H M R O H G R O L I N S O N A H
    E O E D E B N E I P E M C E X D Y R E
    I P D K D A R F O D B E R E T R D Y K
    D H W D C K D E D U I T R T D J K A O
    S A R J Z L A Z R W A B E C E H A N A
    O T U R B A N O B O C O W R O K F Q W
    J N Y R C B U C E I U H O O D J I U R
    U C O W B O Y H A T K T G W H I G B A
    C S W Y S N S T K I O E S N C T B C
    G R O Z R N B C L O C H E M L J G
      C K P X E C D G C F I C W C C
        T D H T Y J D X C C P E D
              V Q O I R G
```

©School Zone Publishing Company 12501

Connect the dots from **I** to **25**.
Color the picture.

5

24 23 21

4 6 7 25 22 20

3 8 19

9

2

1 10 18

11 17

12 16

13 14 15

©School Zone Publishing Company 12501

SUNKEN SHIP SURPRISE

Find and circle the hidden pictures.

battery

treasure chest

sock

clover

snowman

bow tie

heart

safety cone

©School Zone Publishing Company 12501

MACHINES

A machine is a device that makes work easier. Many machines have moving parts that push, pull, twist, squeeze, punch, stamp, or slice. No matter how complex they are, all machines are based on one or more simple machines. The six types of simple machines include the lever, wheel and axle, pulley, inclined plane, wedge, and screw.

Industries use all kinds of machines. Businesses depend on computers and other office machines. Different kinds of machines— such as buses, cars, and airplanes— help people travel across long distances. Trucks, trains, and ships help deliver products.

Think About It!

Think about the ways machines make your life easier. What are some machines you use every day?

BICYCLE
CRANE
DOORKNOB
DRILL
ENGINE
INCLINED PLANE
LEVER
MERRY-GO-ROUND
PLOW
PULLEY
PUMP
ROBOT   SEE GLOSSARY.
SCREW
WEDGE
WHEEL AND AXLE
WINDMILL

```
            W
          N E H A
          I D A E M Z
          S G B S E B S A R H
          Q E D R Q L R G R O B O T Q R P R
          P H O L R O A G R V B I P S O L H
          U E O E H N E N E Y E C U E V O R
          M I R V N D U O D R I L L B X W Y
          P W K E D G D C T A M R L E P D A
          Z A N R L A I P J I X E E C H C N
          L U O X T E O N P S A L Y X F R O
          E J B J A J M J E S C R E W J A J
          U D E A N F I E U R G E R H I N U
          M E R R Y G O R O U N D M T K E C
          Q Z V P B S Y W I N D M I L L G R
            I N C L I N E D P L A N E S O
            X O B I C Y C L E F P W C
            M O X A K J
```

When two or more simple machines work together as one, they form a compound machine.

©School Zone Publishing Company 12501

WHAT A CLIMB!

Find and circle the hidden pictures.

snorkel   watch   party hat   fan   motorcycle   straw   pot   coconut

©School Zone Publishing Company 12501

Connect the dots from 1 to 25.
Color the picture.

©School Zone Publishing Company 12501

BOOKWORM

Help Walter Worm get to the book.

End

©School Zone Publishing Company 12501

DOWN THE SLOPE

Help Renee Raccoon ski to the bottom of the slope.

End

©School Zone Publishing Company 12501

Connect the dots from **1** to **25**.
Color the picture.

SNORKELING FUN

Find and circle the hidden pictures.

feather   wrench   cucumber   orange   wheelbarrow   chair   fork   arrow

©School Zone Publishing Company 12501

BUTTERFLY'S BUDDY

Help Benny Butterfly fly to Allie Alligator.

End

OUT OF THIS WORLD

Help the rocket get to the planet.

End

©School Zone Publishing Company 12501

MEDICINE

Medicine is the science and art of preserving health and treating illness. Medical care has three main elements: prevention, diagnosis, and treatment. In the last few centuries, medicine has progressed greatly. As medical knowledge expanded, physicians found it increasingly difficult to keep up with important advances in the whole field of medicine. Doctors began to spend their final years of training concentrating on a limited area of study. This narrow focus is called specialization.

```
O Q E T M V T X T O N C O L O G Y X W
A E U R D L O G C P X T N O R R Y T D
N M R X Y T R T R H R Q R B T R P H E
E X R U P E D I A T R I C S H I D O R
S H A H W Q D G N H B X N T O N Z H M
T A D E H N E X M A W C E E P Z N E A
H Z I C A R D I O L O G Y T E Q E D T
E D O M Z T D W X M X R X R D E U U O
S T L P A T H O L O G Y X I I N R S L
I Q O T D E A M K L O K V C C V O U O
O J G J P J M J X O J B J S S K L R G
L G Y T N U J E R G Y N E C O L O G Y
O D R U R O L O G Y W C U T X X G E W
G N R W Z R G W C T G X G T U G Y R G
Y X P S Y C H I A T R Y F R P R T Y B
I O P W R B T N V W P R O K R W X R
```

ANESTHESIOLOGY
CARDIOLOGY
DERMATOLOGY
GYNECOLOGY
NEUROLOGY

OBSTETRICS
ONCOLOGY
OPHTHALMOLOGY
ORTHOPEDICS
PATHOLOGY

PEDIATRICS
PSYCHIATRY
RADIOLOGY
SURGERY
UROLOGY

The suffix -ology means "the study of_."
Matched with prefixes "cardio" (heart) or "neuro" (nerves), it can mean the study of the heart or the study of the nervous system.

©School Zone Publishing Company 12501

271

CITIES OF THE WORLD

Thousands of years ago, some Neolithic villages developed into small cities of a few thousand people. As the human population grew, so did the size of the cities. All settlements - from a small village to a giant city - needed four main features to begin and grow. One of those features was advanced thinking, which led to new tools and inventions. Another was a favorable physical environment, including a comfortable climate and the availability of water and food. Settlements also needed social organization - with governments to manage services for the people - and population growth with a diverse range of cultures.

Think About It!

Make a list of some cities you would like to visit someday. What interests you about those cities?

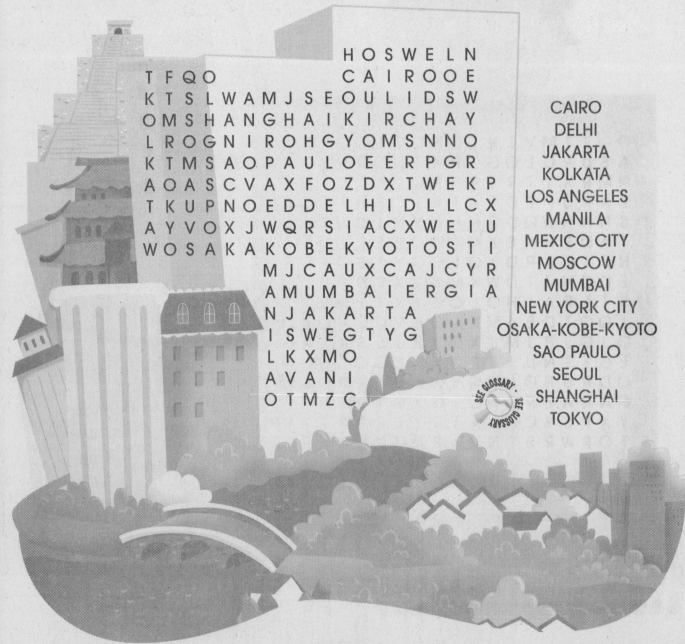

```
            H O S W E L N
T F Q O     C A I R O O E
K T S L W A M J S E O U L I D S W
O M S H A N G H A I K I R C H A Y
L R O G N I R O H G Y O M S N N O
K T M S A O P A U L O E E R P G R
A O A S C V A X F O Z D X T W E K P
T K U P N O E D D E L H I D L L C X
A Y V O X J W Q R S I A C X W E I U
W O S A K A K O B E K Y O T O S T I
    M J C A U X C A J C Y R
    A M U M B A I E R G I A
    N J A K A R T A
    I S W E G T Y G
    L K X M O
    A V A N I
    O T M Z C
```

CAIRO
DELHI
JAKARTA
KOLKATA
LOS ANGELES
MANILA
MEXICO CITY
MOSCOW
MUMBAI
NEW YORK CITY
OSAKA-KOBE-KYOTO
SAO PAULO
SEOUL
SHANGHAI
TOKYO

SEE GLOSSARY · SEE GLOSSARY

272

©School Zone Publishing Company 12501

Connect the dots from I to 25.
Color the picture.

©School Zone Publishing Company 12501

FUN AT THE ARCADE

Find and circle the hidden pictures.

screwdriver   cowboy hat   smiley face   saw   ring   CD   pyramid   bee

©School Zone Publishing Company 12501

Connect the dots from **1** to **25**.

Color the picture.

©School Zone Publishing Company 12501

THAT'S NUTTY!

Help Susan Squirrel get to the acorns.

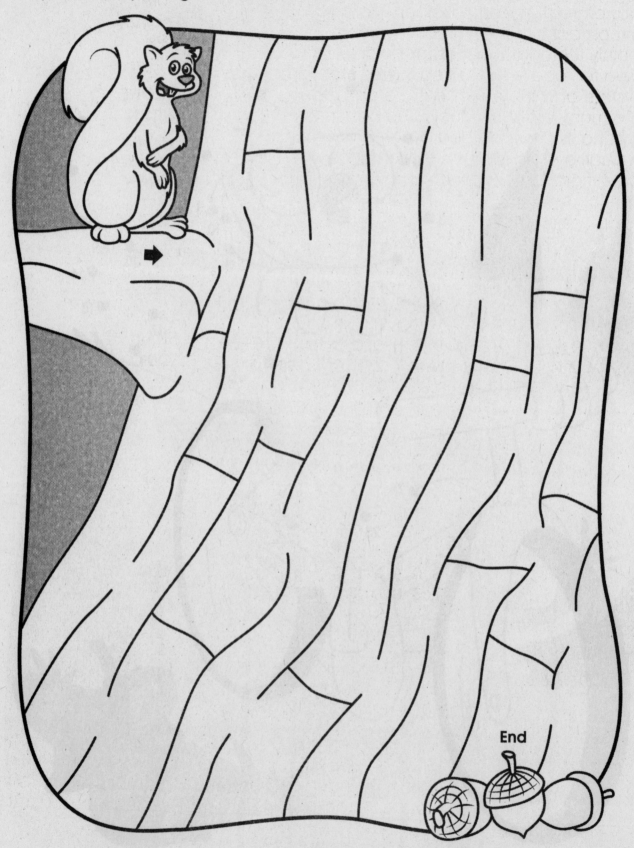

End

276

©School Zone Publishing Company 12501

MOLLUSKS

A mollusk is a soft-bodied animal that has no bones. Most mollusks have a hard shell that protects their soft bodies. Mollusks live in most parts of the world and are used mainly for food. The most popular kinds used for food in the United States are clams, oysters, and snails. Mollusks are also made into many useful products. The best known product is probably pearls, which are found in pearl oysters. Mollusks make up the largest group of water animals.

Think About It!

In what ways are mollusks different from other sea creatures? In what ways are they the same?

ABALONE
CHITON
CLAM
COCKLE
CONCH
COWRIE
LIMPET
MOTHER-OF-PEARL
OCTOPUS
OYSTER
SCALLOP
SNAIL
SQUID

SEE GLOSSARY

```
X D K T D X
Z L I M P E T O B Y
L T V T P T M T P X T N O
X M R C O W R I E Z R Q R V M
R X N R C X V P T H C H I T O N
R F H L H T O D G N O O X N R T N C
U M P D C O M W P Y Z N C Z R H Z R
R W T K C P D X Q W X C T W X E D Y
H C Z S Q U I D W A Z H R X D R Z T
C T O Q P S T R T B T B Z X V O T N
O L N C T D Z V O A P O Q V T F V
Z A B K S N A I L W J B J W P K
G M T L U X Z O Y S T E R E
    C X E O N N C W C R T A
    R G W E P G X G T R
    Q K R F X Z T F R L
    B S C A L L O P K R
    T S H C X C H D
```

©School Zone Publishing Company 12501

FISH

Fish are of great importance to human beings. They provide food for millions of people. They are caught by fishing enthusiasts for sport, and they are kept as pets.

All fish have two main features in common. First, they have a backbone, which makes them vertebrates. Second, they breathe mainly by means of gills.

Nearly all fish are cold-blooded, which means that they cannot regulate their body temperature. Their temperature changes based on the temperature of the water around them. Almost all fish have a streamlined body and fins that they use for swimming.

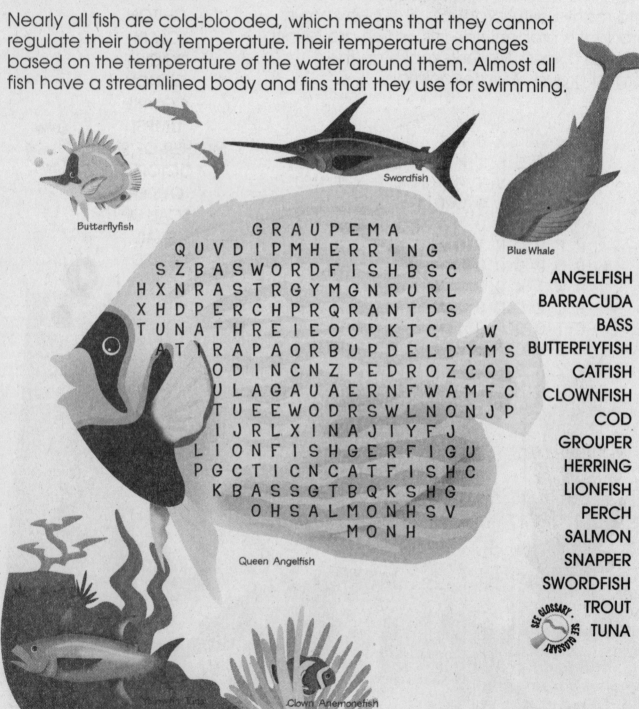

Butterflyfish

Swordfish

Blue Whale

```
            G R A U P E M A
      Q U V D I P M H E R R I N G
      S Z B A S W O R D F I S H B S C
      H X N R A S T R G Y M G N R U R L
      X H D P E R C H P R Q R A N T D S
      T U N A T H R E I E O O P K T C      W
      A T I R A P A O R B U P D E L D Y M S
      O D I N C N Z P E D R O Z C O D
      U L A G A U A E R N F W A M F C
      T U E E W O D R S W L N O N J P
      I J R L X I N A J I Y F J
      L I O N F I S H G E R F I G U
      P G C T I C N C A T F I S H C
      K B A S S G T B Q K S H G
      O H S A L M O N H S V
            M O N H
```

Queen Angelfish

ANGELFISH
BARRACUDA
BASS
BUTTERFLYFISH
CATFISH
CLOWNFISH
COD
GROUPER
HERRING
LIONFISH
PERCH
SALMON
SNAPPER
SWORDFISH
TROUT
TUNA

Yellowfin Tuna

Clown Anemonefish

©School Zone Publishing Company 12501

Connect the dots from **1** to **25**.
Color the picture.

©School Zone Publishing Company 12501

MONSTERS UNDER YOUR BED

Find and circle the hidden pictures.

butterfly   mushroom   bowling pin   milk carton   clam   salt shaker   banana   cherries

280

©School Zone Publishing Company 12501

Connect the dots from 1 to 25.
Color the picture.

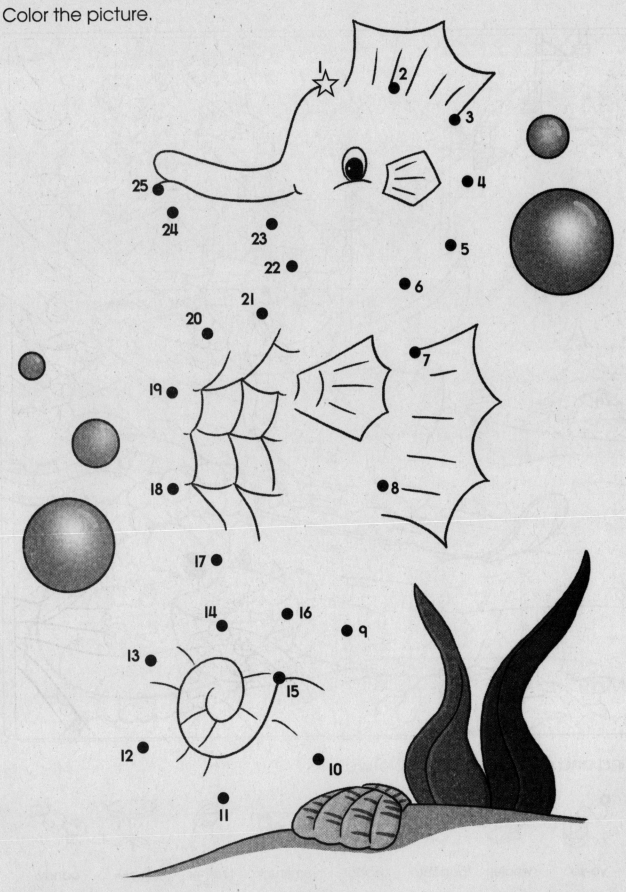

©School Zone Publishing Company 12501

A DAY ON THE SLOPES

Find and circle the hidden pictures.

yo-yo   whale   popcorn   paper   semitruck   feather   table   candy

282

©School Zone Publishing Company 12501

A DAY ON THE HILL

Help Amy Ant and Alexander Ant get to the center of the anthill.

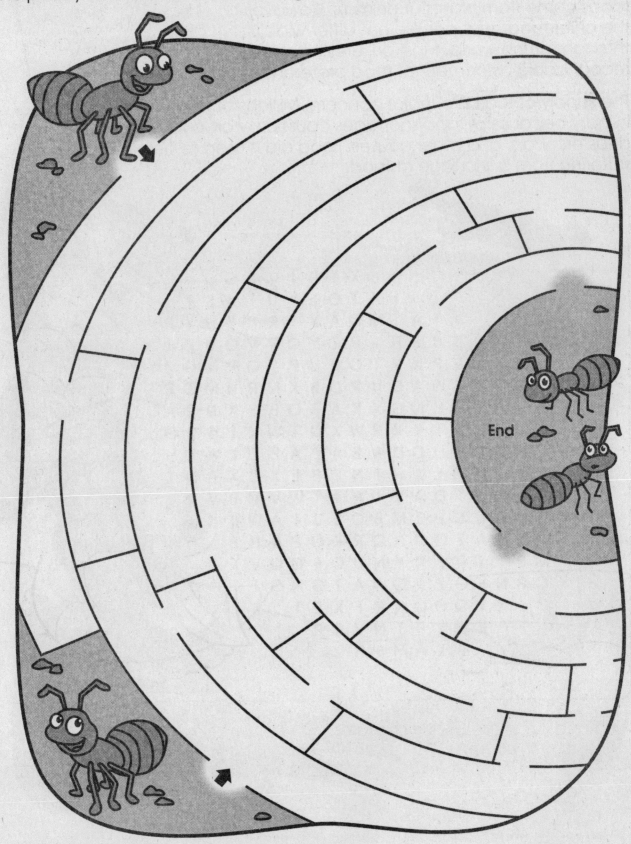

End

©School Zone Publishing Company 12501

FOOD

Food is one of our most basic needs. All living things must have food to live. Almost all foods come from plants or animals. However, the chief foods that people eat differ widely throughout the world. Most cultures have a recognizable assortment of food preferences.

The supply of food is a major concern. Millions of people go hungry because of food shortages caused by crop failures, natural disasters, wars, and other causes. Food aid is used to help people suffering from a shortage of food.

Think About It!

What are some ethnic dishes that you would like to try? Think about the culture from where the food comes.

```
        X T R I C E G
      I X T O L Y U T W S T
    V T A T M Q A X T R P Y H Y P
    R S U S H I P Z Y Q R V O U P I
    X N R P X R T O R U P Y O R M G Z
    B E E F W A D U R O B X N R H M C Z
    M A Z I H N G X K A B O B S X U R A
    K U E K S T K X H W X D T W X L S Z D
    R H N D L H D C D W E A P A E L L A T U
    T D P T Q M L W H T N T B E X C X P N T
    X U X N I T D A V I R I T W V M B V R
    N C H E E S E J M B C L J I A W J K
    P K U G A Z O U H Q R K G E R H E
    M S T I R F R Y N U C E C Q V X
    C P N E G Z R G W A T G N G T
      X T Q O Q K R F X E T
        P W R B T N V R P
          B L A M B H
```

BEEF
CHEESE
CHICKEN
CURRY
DUCK
FISH
HUMMUS
KABOBS
LAMB
PAELLA
PIZZA
PORK
RICE
SPAGHETTI
STIR-FRY
SUSHI

SEE GLOSSARY

©School Zone Publishing Company 12501

Connect the dots from **A** to **J**.
Color the picture.

©School Zone Publishing Company 12501

Connect the Dots

HOOK, LINE, AND SINKER

Help Felicity Fish swim to the worm.

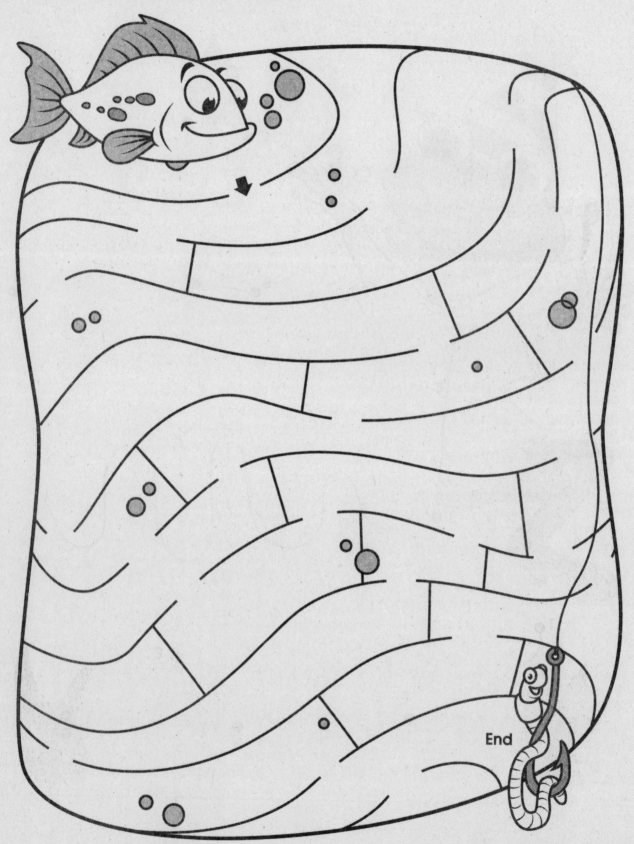

End

©School Zone Publishing Company 12501

Connect the dots from **A** to **J**.

Color the picture.

©School Zone Publishing Company 12501

287

THE DINOS IN CONCERT

Find and circle the hidden pictures.

moon   glasses   ladybug   house   fish   crown   button   domino

©School Zone Publishing Company 12501

COOKING

Cooking is the preparation of food for eating by applying heat. Cooking makes food more appetizing and digestible. Cooking also destroys harmful bacteria.

From prehistoric times until the 1800s, cooking was done mostly over open fires or wood stoves. Gas stoves became popular during the late 1800s, and the electric stove became popular in the 1930s. Microwave ovens were introduced in the 1950s. Today, cooking is much easier and faster than ever.

Think About It!

Think about how advances in cooking technology have changed the types of food that people eat.

```
T B Z B Q R F
X R G E R U A U O R
H W O D R I O O X K Y H Y
D E H N E I L E W I E E X E
P K C T D X L W B O I L X E D
S I M M E R D L X E X R A D R E
B Y W Q O L T R M R C B E X C X
P R E S S U R E C O O K W V O
I E J T J P J M J A L R B J
L U M E M N U W Q S U G E
J D A C X P O N T C
T M G Z R G
```

BAKE
BOIL
BROIL
FRY

GRILL
PRESSURE COOK
ROAST
SIMMER
STEAM

©School Zone Publishing Company 12501

BACK TO SCHOOL

Find and circle the hidden pictures.

 seashell   candle   magnet   bottle   push pin   earring   lamp   mailbox

290

©School Zone Publishing Company 12501

OUT OF THE NEST

Help the egg get back to its nest.

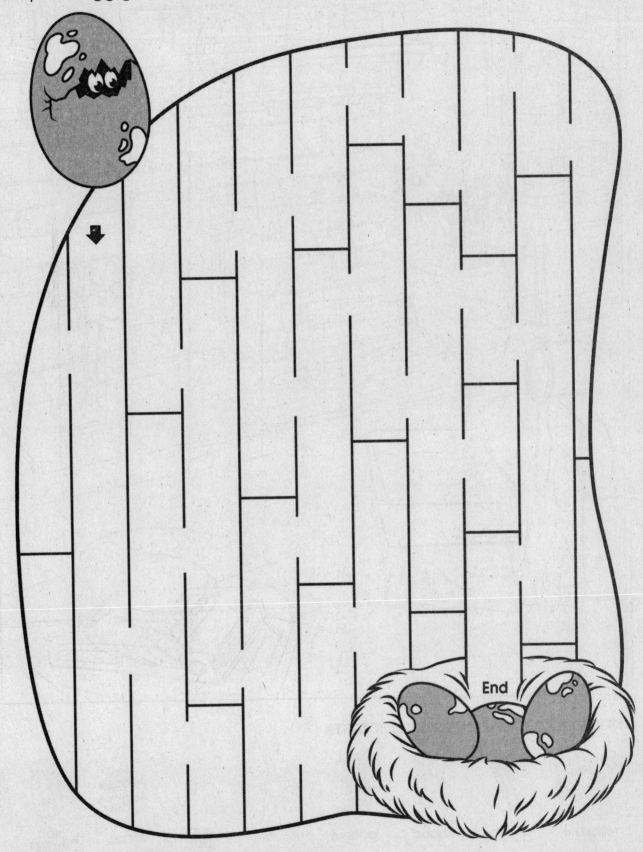

End

©School Zone Publishing Company 12501

DOZING BY THE FIRE

Find and circle the hidden pictures.

| plate | crayon | hand | peanut | sun | baseball bat | rose | salt shaker |

292

©School Zone Publishing Company 12501

FOUNDING FATHERS

During the early 1700s, the U.S. was a group of colonies governed by Great Britain. By mid-century, the colonists became angry with their lack of self-government and a series of unfair taxes and laws. In 1773, the colonists rebelled against the taxes on tea by boarding British ships and dumping tea into Boston Harbor in an act that became known as the Boston Tea Party.

The British reacted by passing several harsh measures that became known as the Intolerable Acts. This united opposition to British rule led to the Continental Congress. Representatives from the colonies met to petition King George III and organize a new government.

These representatives and other leaders who signed founding documents into law became known as the Founding Fathers of the United States. The Declaration of Independence was adopted in Philadelphia on July 4, 1776. The war lasted until 1783.

```
                              L K J C
                              T O X P J Q M X
                              S J S Q P I C A
S R O P L S Y A S D R S X P G N S E N I S A S M S O P
R W E I N I X R M A R S H A L L W K A E D R Y C R A Y
H E A H K E V N H G W O B I N T P N E H J N H H T X O
E V M S D E H I W I S C K C U X S K R X E P R E Z R
D K H D H D A U N P Q F D A W U X K Y D F U Y N X M
V P A B Q I S N D G E R R Y R M B F D Q F D A R D A
V N A V T N M S J S A B E Z C H R L A E A N Y A Q
U C S I H E G P X J T O X I B W A T N R O E S I Y
O O J B J G Q T J R B O J M E C N J E S J N F P J
Y C D E R A W K O R P G N R H I K A X O R G Z I U
I K C M A D I S O N C R H A M I L T O N C T L X P C
Q T G R N A Q T U R T G O N P M I T H M O N R O E G
A S D M S M U P T X A E A P A I N E S M R I M J I D
G M T S Y S I A S K S U R B I W X O U Y T O Q C S K
R W B E J T M Q W F P O V R A N D O L P H R C T N Y
```

ADAMS	JAY	MCHENRY
FRANKLIN	JEFFERSON	MONROE
GERRY	LIVINGSTON	PAINE
HAMILTON	MADISON	RANDOLPH
HANCOCK	MARSHALL	WASHINGTON

©School Zone Publishing Company 12501

Connect the dots from **A** to **K**.
Color the picture.

©School Zone Publishing Company 12501

THE BIG CHEESE

Help Mattie Mouse find the cheese.

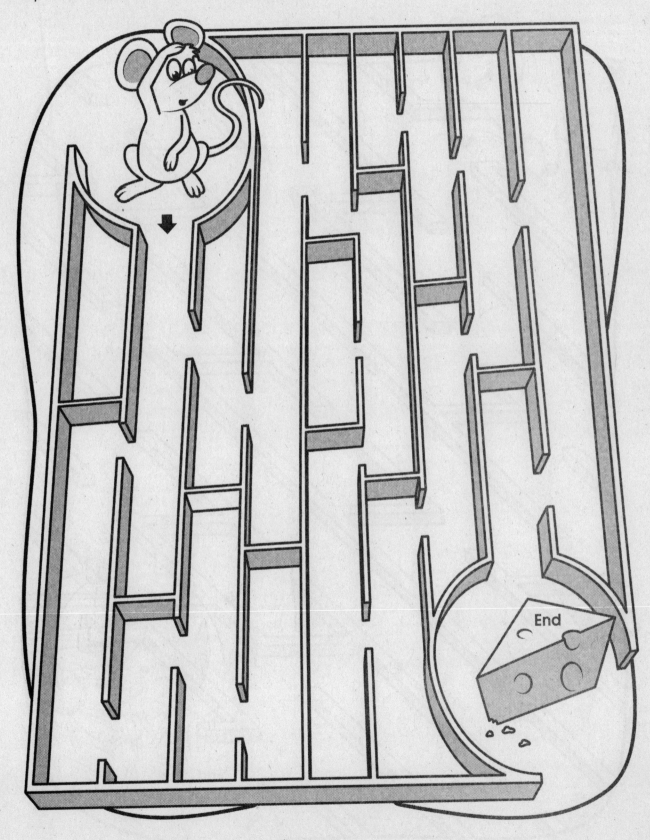

End

©School Zone Publishing Company 12501

PIG PEN

Help Paula Pig get to her dinner.

End

296

©School Zone Publishing Company 12501

Connect the dots from **A** to **J**.
Color the picture.

©School Zone Publishing Company 12501

COMMUNICATION

Communication means sharing information. People communicate mainly by speaking and writing. Facial expressions and body movements are nonverbal forms of communication. Most of our communication is personal, the exchange of information with one or a few people. Mass communication involves many people and uses different kinds of communicative media, such as televisions, computers, newspapers, books, and magazines.

Language is the organized system of signals or symbols used to communicate. Use of languages began in prehistoric times, although scholars are unsure about the exact origin since words and symbols vary across countries and cultures.

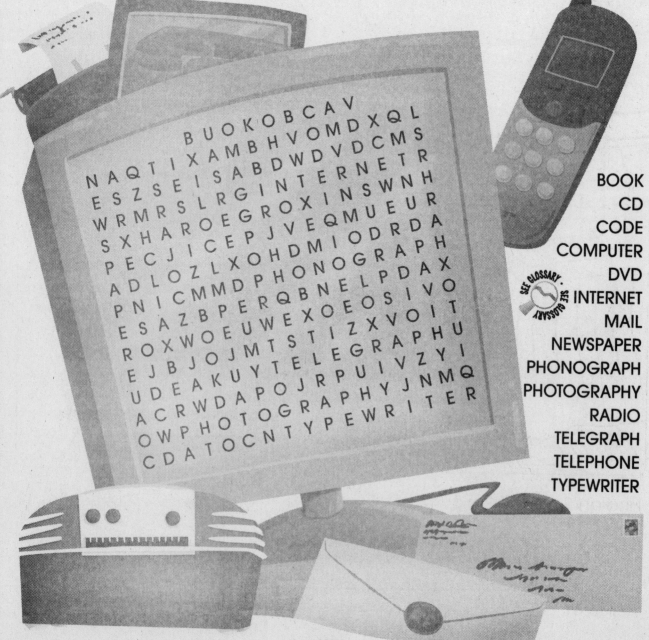

BOOK
CD
CODE
COMPUTER
DVD
INTERNET
MAIL
NEWSPAPER
PHONOGRAPH
PHOTOGRAPHY
RADIO
TELEGRAPH
TELEPHONE
TYPEWRITER

©School Zone Publishing Company 12501

ABRACADABRA!

Find and circle the hidden pictures.

tuna can   magnifying glass   sailboat   pie slice   leaf   lemon   squirrel   pot

©School Zone Publishing Company 12501

Connect the dots from **A** to **L**.
Color the picture.

300

©School Zone Publishing Company 12501

PENCIL TRAIL

Help the pencil get to the bottom of the page.

End

©School Zone Publishing Company 12501

OUT OF THE WATER!

Help Barry Bear surf to the beach.

End

©School Zone Publishing Company 12501

Connect the dots from **A** to **M**.
Color the picture.

DESERT OASIS

Help Cory Camel get a drink of water.

End

©School Zone Publishing Company 12501

SONGBIRDS

All birds have feathers, and birds are the only animals that have feathers. Birds hatch from eggs. Most birds remain in the nest where their parents feed and protect them until they can take care of themselves. Birds live in all parts of the world, from the polar regions to the tropics. They are found in deserts and on islands, in grasslands and forests, on farmlands and mountaintops, and in cities. There are over 9,000 different kinds of birds. Many birds have beautiful colors or sing sweet songs.

Think About It!

Why don't birds fall out of the trees when they go to sleep? Hint: It has to do with their feet.

```
      J X
      V A R K
R L A R K M X Y T R
O M B O B O L I N K F
B U R F S C H W O D I W
I C H I C K A D E E N A
N D T K Q I C M Q X C R S
C A R D I N A L L D H B Z
  W C T S G I A O R T L T S C
  X R L N B O R I O L E P M W A
  P E Q I J C E M J R L X Y A T
  I N R T V S P A R R O W R L B G
  D C N U T H A T C H Z T L I C R
            T Z O R G U
            W D X
```

BOBOLINK
CARDINAL
CATBIRD
CHICKADEE

FINCH
LARK
MOCKINGBIRD
NUTHATCH
ORIOLE

ROBIN
SPARROW
SWALLOW
WARBLER
WREN

SEE GLOSSARY

©School Zone Publishing Company 12501

305

SWINGING BY

Help Monica Monkey swing home to her tree house.

End

©School Zone Publishing Company 12501

FALL FUN

Find and circle the hidden pictures.

carrot   mitten   pizza slice   strawberry   hourglass   square ruler   shovel   balloon

307

©School Zone Publishing Company 12501

MUD BATH

Find and circle the hidden pictures.

mug   bread   ladder   fish   leaf   bow tie   football   bolt

©School Zone Publishing Company 12501

MAYAN RUINS

Help Lucy Llama get to the ground.

End

©School Zone Publishing Company 12501

IN THE TREE

Help Carrie Cat get down from the tree.

End

©School Zone Publishing Company 12501

Connect the dots from **A** to **O**.
Color the picture.

©School Zone Publishing Company 12501

Connect the dots from **A** to **P**.
Color the picture.

©School Zone Publishing Company 12501

LANDING PAD

Help the helicopter land safely on the landing pad.

End

©School Zone Publishing Company 12501

FRUIT TREES

People throughout the world eat fruits, nuts, and other tree products. The greatest variety of fruit trees grow in tropical and subtropical regions. These trees produce such fruits as avocados, grapefruits, mangoes, and oranges. Cooler, temperate regions have fewer kinds of fruit trees, but several kinds are widely known. For example, orchards in the United States produce lots of apples, cherries, and peaches.

Think About It!

What kind of fruit trees grow near your home?

```
V T Y A P J L E
A R X Y T V T R Z R Q G
C P P R M X O G F M U E R O M
F Z E P W O C H E R R Y A R H L
M Q O A L Q A X M E W C P E X E
O Y T K H R E D O L O D T E X E M
L V A P R I C O T X R X R F D R O
I T E L Q L W R T N A B E R C X N
V L N E P D E P Z X N P L U M B V
E A J M A N G O P X G E B I W J K
U L E F N U J D L E A E T H E
D I R X E M N U E C C F T
N R M Z R G W O T H X V
R P E Q K F I G
```

APPLE
APRICOT
AVOCADO
CHERRY

FIG
GRAPEFRUIT
LEMON
LIME

MANGO
OLIVE
ORANGE
PEACH
PEAR
PLUM

314

©School Zone Publishing Company 12501

FRIENDLY DRAGON

Help the knight get to the dragon.

End

©School Zone Publishing Company 12501

MAKING A MONSTER MOVIE

Find and circle the hidden pictures.

peach   marker   cane   bandage   vase   sock   plane   whale

316

©School Zone Publishing Company 12501

Find and circle the hidden pictures.

door

bell

helicopter

boxing glove

inner tube

tooth

soap

cinnamon roll

©School Zone Publishing Company 12501

Connect the dots from **A** to **N**.

Color the picture.

©School Zone Publishing Company 12501

GLOSSARY

Use a dictionary to learn about vocabulary words that aren't defined in this glossary.

abdomen: the tail end of an insect.

Adriatic Sea: part of the Mediterranean Sea between Italy and the Balkan Peninsula.

Aegean Sea: part of the Mediterranean Sea between Greece and Turkey.

allosaurus: a meat-eating dinosaur with big, curved teeth. It walked on two legs.

amateur: someone who plays a sport for pleasure rather than payment.

Anchorage: the largest city in Alaska.

antennae: the feelers on the head of an insect.

apatosaurus: a huge, plant-eating dinosaur with a long neck and an arched back.

astronomy: the study of objects outside the Earth's atmosphere.

avalanche: snow drifts in mountainous areas that rush downward.

Badlands: a national park in South Dakota with ravines, cliffs, and prehistoric fossils.

Baltic Sea: a sea in northern Europe.

Barents Sea: part of the Arctic Ocean near northeast Europe.

barnacle: a type of shellfish that attaches itself to boats, rocks, and other animals.

beret: a soft cap with a flat top that is usually made of wool.

Bering Sea: part of the north Pacific Ocean, north of the Aleutian Islands.

Black Sea: a sea between Europe and Asia.

blizzard: a severe winter storm with dry, driving snow, strong winds, and intense cold.

boccie: a game that is like lawn bowling.

brachiosaurus: a tall, plant-eating dinosaur with a long neck and a massive, sloping body.

camouflage: the act of hiding by means of disguise.

canopy: the top layer of rainforest trees.

Canyonlands: a national park in Utah with canyons, mesas, and 1,000-year-old Native American rock carvings.

capybara: the largest living rodent. It looks like a large guinea pig with no tail and webbed feet.

Caribbean Sea: part of the Atlantic Ocean near Central and South America.

caribou: a large reindeer.

Carlsbad Caverns: a national park in New Mexico with underground caves.

cartilage: the strong, elastic tissue that connects bones and forms human ears and noses.

castle: a fortified residence, usually for royalty or the wealthy in medieval times.

catamaran: a sailboat with twin hulls and a deck between them.

cathedral: a principal Christian church.

cello: a large string instrument that is played with a bow and rests on the ground.

cellophane: a clear plastic used as a food covering.

China Sea: part of the Pacific Ocean near China.

chinchilla: a rodent native to South America that has very soft, gray fur.

church: a building for Christian Worship.

cicada: a type of insect that makes a loud, shrill noise.

clarinet: a wind instrument played by blowing across a reed in the mouthpiece.

cloche: a formal woman's hat shaped like a bell.

cobra: a large, poisonous snake that spreads its skin like a hood when agitated.

cockroach: an insect with a flattened body that is a household pest.

cod: a type of fish found in the Atlantic Ocean.

cold-blooded: animals, such as reptiles and fish, whose body temperatures change according to their surroundings.

comet: a celestial body made of mostly ice and dust that develops one or more long tails when near the sun.

continental shelf: a shallow area of the ocean floor along the coast.

coral: a hard material made of the skeletons of tiny sea animals.

coral reef: a ridge of rocks and coral found mostly in warm and shallow tropical seas.

Coral Sea: part of the Pacific Ocean near Australia.

cotton gin: a machine for seperating the cotton fibers from the seeds.

croquet: an outdoor game that uses mallets to hit wooden balls through wire hoops in the ground.

curry: an Indian dish that is seasoned with a variety of strong spices.

cuscus: a type of possom that is most active at night.

Death Valley: a national park in California and Nevada. This desert is the lowest land surface in the U. S.

Denali: a national park in Alaska with Mt. McKinley, the highest mountain in North America.

desert: an area that has very little rainfall.

dragonfly: a type of insect with two sets of wings and a long slender body.

earthquake: a series of vibrations caused by movements in the Earth's crust.

emergent trees: the very tall trees that grow above the top layer of a rainforest.

eoraptor: a small, meat-eating dinosaur that walked on two legs.

Everglades: a national park in Florida that is a subtropical wilderness.

extinct: refers to a type of animal or plant that has died out. None are living today.

fez: a cone-shaped, flat-crowned hat with a tassel that is usually made of red felt.

fiction: an invented or imagined story about people and places that are not real.

flood: a flowing of water on land that is not normally submerged.

floor: the dark ground of a rainforest.

flute: a wind instrument played by blowing across a hole at one end and covering holes to change the tones.

forest: an area covered with trees and underbrush, also called a woodland.

fossil: the remains of a plant or an animal from millions of years ago preserved as a rock.

galaxies: a very large group of stars found throughout the universe. Ours is called the Milky Way Galaxy.

gecko: a small tropical lizard that is usually active at night.

glacier: a large mass of ice that moves slowly across a continent.

Glacier: a national park in Montana with glaciers and lakes.

gong: a percussion instrument that is a metal disk that makes a hollow, echoing sound when struck.

Grand Canyon: a national park in Arizona. The Colorado River cut the one-mile-deep canyon.

grassland: an area where most of the vegetation is grasses, sometimes called a prairie.

guppy: a tiny freshwater fish that is a common pet.

habitat: a plant or animal's natural environment.

hadrasaur: a common, duck-billed, plant-eating dinosaur.

harp: a large, triangular string instrument that is played by plucking the strings.

heron: a type of bird that lives near water and has long, thin legs and a long beak.

Honolulu: the capital of Hawaii.

hula: a native Hawaiian dance.

hummus: a paste of pureed chickpeas and sesame oil eaten as a dip or sandwich spread.

hurricane: a violent tropical storm in the Atlantic Ocean with high winds and rain.

hydrofoil: a motorboat that has fins attached to lift the boat from the water when at a certain speed.

inclined plane: a surface that makes a slanted angle with the horizon. An example is a ramp.

invertebrate: an animal without a backbone.

jacana: a small tropical bird with long toes for walking on water plants.

judo: a sport in which two people use quick movements to try to throw each other to the ground.

Juneau: the capital of Alaska.

junk: a wooden, flat-bottomed sailing vessel used in China and the East Indies.

katydid: a green insect resembling a grasshopper. The male rubs its front wings to make a shrill noise.

kayak: a small boat propelled by hand with a paddle.

kelp: a large and edible type of brown seaweed.

kingfisher: a small bird that lives near water and has bright feathers and a long bill.

lemur: a primate native to Madagascar that has a longish muzzle, large eyes, very soft fur, and a long, furry tail.

lever: a bar that transmits force to pry something.

limpet: a type of sea animal with a protective shell. It clamps to rocks with a muscular foot.

llama: a long-neck South American animal that is related to the camel but is smaller and does not have a hump.

luge: a one- or two-person sled for racing down a chute.

macaw: a large parrot with colored feathers and a loud voice.

mandrill: a large baboon. The male has a ribbed blue and red face.

mantis: a large insect that clasps its front legs as if in prayer.

marmoset: a small monkey with a long tail.

©School Zone Publishing Company 12501

GLOSSARY

marmot: a stout, short-legged rodent that has coarse fur, a bushy tail, and small ears.

marshland: an area with marshes, swamps, bogs, and other low, wet land.

mayfly: a type of insect with delicate wings.

Mediterranean Sea: a sea between Europe, Africa, and Asia.

meteorologist: a scientist who studies weather and the earth.

mimicry: the practice of copying.

mosque: a Muslim temple or place of worship.

mountain: an area with a much higher elevation than its surroundings.

museum: a building where works of art, scientific specimens, or other valuable objects are stored and displayed.

mushers: people who compete in dogsled races.

myna: a dark brown bird that can imitate the human voice.

Neolithic: the last period of the Stone Age.

nighthawk: a short-billed, short-legged bird with spotted wings.

North Sea: part of the Atlantic Ocean between Great Britain and the European mainland.

nuthatch: a small bird with a short tail and a sharp beak.

oboe: a wind instrument played by blowing across a double reed in the mouthpiece.

okapi: a mammal that resembles a giraffe but with a much shorter neck and striped legs.

Olympic: a national park in Washington with ocean, mountain, and rainforest habitats.

orangutan: a large ape with long, reddish-brown hair and long, strong arms.

organ: a keyboard instrument with one or more keyboards and pipes of different lengths.

ostrich: a very large, two-toed bird that does not fly.

paella: a rice dish that may also contain meat, seafood, and/or vegetables.

pagoda: a temple or sacred building usually found in Asia.

paleontology: the study of fossils and ancient life forms, including dinosaurs.

papayas: a large, yellow, melonlike fruit.

parasite: an organism that depends on another for existence or support without doing much in return.

peacock: a type of bird. The male peacock displays brightly colored, upright feathers.

Pearl Harbor: a U.S. naval base in Hawaii. Japanese forces attacked Pearl Harbor during World War II.

phonograph: an instrument that uses a needle and a revolving disc to reproduce sounds.

piranha: a type of fish that eats other fish and sometimes larger animals that enter the water.

planetarium: a building that uses moving projectors to display stars, planets, and other visible objects in space.

plankton: tiny animals and plants that float in bodies of water.

platypus: an egg-laying mammal from Australia with webbed feet and a broad bill.

polar ice: the layer of ice at the North or South Pole.

Polo: a game in which two teams of four players on horseback use long mallets to hit a small ball.

pontoon: a flat-bottomed boat.

pulley: a wheel that uses a rope or chain in a groove to transmit power.

pyramid: a building shaped like a triangle. Most pyramids were tombs or temple platforms.

quetzal: a type of bird with red and green feathers. The male has very long tail feathers.

rainforest: a tropical forest with high annual rainfall.

Red Sea: part of the Indian Ocean between Africa and Arabia.

Redwood: a national park in California with the world's largest living tree.

roadrunner: a small bird with brown or black feathers and a long tail. It runs quickly across the ground.

rockslide: when a mass of rocks suddenly dislodges and falls.

Saguaro: a national park in Arizona with a cactus forest that includes large saguaro cacti.

salamander: an amphibian that looks like a lizard but has soft, moist skin instead of scales.

sampan: a small boat that typically has a cabin. It is used mostly in rivers and harbors in eastern Asia.

saxophone: a brass wind instrument with keys for the fingers.

screw: a stick with a spiral thread on its surface and a place to turn it at one end.

scrubland: an area covered with low trees and shrubs.

sea anemone: a sea animal with a tube-shaped body and circles of tentacles around its mouth.

sea fan: colorful coral with a flat, fanlike shape.

Shenandoah: a national park in Virginia with the Blue Ridge Mountains and Skyline Drive.

skink: a type of lizard with flat, overlapping, smooth scales.

skyscraper: a tall building usually used for offices.

sloop: a boat with one mast and one triangular sail.

sloth: a type of mammal with long legs, curved claws, and shaggy fur. It moves slowly and hangs upside down in trees.

sombrero: a hat with a high crown and wide brim.

squash: a game played by two people who use racquets to hit a small, rubber ball against the walls of an enclosed court.

stadium: a sports arena with tiers of seats for spectators.

stegosaurus: a plant-eating dinosaur with two rows of spines down its back and long, heavy spikes on its tail.

sushi: raw seafood, often served with cold rice and vegetables.

swallow: a type of bird with a short bill, long pointed wings, and a forked tail.

swamp: an area of wet, spongy land.

synagogue: a Jewish temple or place of worship.

synthesizer: an electronic instrument that can make a variety of sounds and imitate other instruments.

tamarin: a type of mammal that resembles a monkey with a long tail and silky fur.

tapir: a large animal that looks like a pig with a long snout and hooves.

tarsier: a small mammal that resembles a monkey with large eyes and padded fingers and toes.

Tasman Sea: part of the Pacific Ocean between Australia and New Zealand. **telegraph:** a device that sends messages over long distances by using a code of electronical signals.

temple: a place for religious worship.

termite: a type of insect that eats wood and resembles an ant.

thorax: the part of an insect's body between its head and its abdomen.

titi: a small, red or gray monkey.

tomb: a place where a person is buried or a building that is a memorial to a dead person.

tornado: a violent windstorm that can be identified by a long, funnel-shaped cloud that extends to the ground.

toucan: a brightly colored tropical bird with a large beak.

tower: a vertical part of a building that is much taller than the building around it, sometimes a prison or fortress.

triangle: a triangular percussion instrument that is struck with a metal rod.

triceratops: a plant-eating dinosaur with a short frill behind its head and three horns.

trombone: a brass wind instrument with a long, bent tube that slides back and forth to play different tones.

tsunami: huge ocean waves caused by undersea earthquakes or volcanoes.

tuatara: a large reptile that looks like a lizard. It can live over 100 years.

tuba: a large, brass wind instrument that makes a deep sound. It has several valves to change the tones.

tundra: an extremely cold and dry area. Part of the soil is frozen all year.

turban: a head covering made by winding a long cloth.

typhoon: a violent tropical storm in the Pacific Ocean or China Sea with high winds and rain.

tyrannosaurus: a large, meat-eating dinosaur that walked on two legs.

understory: the middle layer of trees in the rainforest.

universe: everything that physically exists.

vertebrate: an animal with a backbone.

violin: a string instrument with four strings that are played with a bow.

volcano: a vent in the earth's crust that allows lava, steam, and ash to come out.

warm-blooded: animals, such as mammals, whose body temperatures must remain constant.

wedge: a piece of wood or iron with a thin edge that is used for splitting or lifting something.

wheel and axle: a grooved wheel that is turned by a rope or chain to lift something.

woodland: an area covered with trees, also called a forest.

Yellowstone: a national park in Idaho, Montana, and Wyoming. It has the world's greatest geyser area.

Yosemite: a national park in California with mountain scenery, including gorges and waterfalls.

©School Zone Publishing Company 12501